GARY SPRATT

Dimensions
Cup - 3-3/4"X4-3/4".
Beaver L.3-1/8"

MicMac Belt Cup
Early 19th Century
Wood with hide thong

www.garysprattfineart.com

P.O. Box 162, Rutherford, CA 94573 • Tel. 707-963-4022 - Fax. 707-963-1742

David F.

Rosenthal

Art of Oceania and Related Books

Since 1987

Lime container stopper
Middle Sepik River, New Guinea
late 19th century or older, 43cm.
Illustrated: *OCEANIC ART*, A.J.P. Meyer,
Cologne, 1995; Volume I, page 231, plate 246.

By Appointment
2158 Sutter Street, San Francisco, CA 94115
phone/fax (415) 922 · 8978
email: dfr@oceanic-art.net

ANTHROPOS
F I N E A R T

860 Glenneyre Street • Laguna Beach, CA 92651 • USA
Tel: 949.376.5754 • Fax: 949.443.4120 • E-mail: info@anthroposgallery.com

www.anthroposgallery.com

Above: Chilkat Dancing Blanket, Tlingit, ca. 19th C., Dimensions: 48 in. x 72 in. (122 cm. x 183 cm.)
Below: Colima Dog, Protoclassic, ca. 100 BC to AD 250, Length: 13 in. (33 cm.)

Tolai Lor Mask, New Britain. H: 40.5" (102.9cm). Photo by Suzanne Motheral.

LEWIS/WARA GALLERY
K I R B Y   K A L L A S - L E W I S

PETER-MICHAEL BOYD

Traditional African Art & Material Culture

SEATTLE

petermichael.boyd@att.net

Senufo
Côte d'Ivoire
Wood. H: 15"

Mahamadou Sylla

By appointment only

Tribal Arts GUIDE

Vol. 4

Western North America
The United States and Canada

Listings are alphabetical by state and then by city

Cover Illustrations

The Fine Arts Building at the 1894 California Midwinter International Exposition in San Francisco.
Photo courtesy of the San Francisco Public Library.

Basket Bowl. Maidu, California.
Photo Courtesy of the Oakland Museum of California.

Gold Mouth Mask. Nasca, Peru. AD 200–600.
Ritual Mask. East Sepik Province, Papua New Guinea. AD 650–780.
Both photos courtesy of the Fine Arts Museums of San Francisco. Mask Photo by John Bigelow Taylor, NYC.

Tribal Arts Guide - **WESTERN NORTH AMERICA**

INTRODUCTION

Human occupation of the Western Seaboard of North America closely relates to the end of the last ice age. There are conflicting hypotheses about origins and settlement patterns of early man in the New World, but most agree that western North America was settled in the immediate wake of the retreat of glacial ice more than 10,000 years ago. One of the earliest known human artifacts from the region is an antler projectile point from the Manis Mastodon Site on Washington's Olympic Peninsula, west of Seattle, that has been dated to approximately 12,000 BP. A cedar basket fragment from a nearby site dating to 2900 BP is an interesting intermediary to the remarkable art traditions that would develop along the coast. These include some of the great examples of world art, ranging from the surreal masks of the Arctic Yup'ik to the totemic carvings of the Northwest Coast and from the remarkable lithics of the Columbia River Gorge to the sensitive baskets of the Native Californians.

Early European contact with the West Coast was made by Spanish sea explorers after the Papal Bull of 1493 granted Spain dominion over such New World discoveries as the Pacific Ocean. In 1532, Hernán Cortés ordered the construction of ships on the Pacific coast of New Spain to further expansion of Spain's power. The following year the tip of Baja California was discovered by Fortún Jiménez, a Basque mutineer who was killed there in a skirmish with Pericú Indians, an early casualty of a massive cultural conflict that would decimate the Native populations of the West Coast. In 1542, Juan Rodríguez Cabrillo sailed north from New Spain looking for the Straits of Anian (the Northwest Passage), a fabled northern sea connection between the Atlantic and Pacific. He is believed to have sailed as far north as the contemporary California/Oregon border, exploring and mapping as he went.

Spanish sightings of the Alta California coast became frequent after 1565, when Manila galleons traveling from the Philippines to Acapulco began riding the North Pacific Current, which provided landfall near the Mendocino coast in Northern

Presentation basket woven by Maria Marta (Chumash, b. 1766), c. 1822.
Phoebe Hearst Museum of Anthropology, University of California at Berkeley (1-22478).

California, though sometimes this occurred further north. The *San Francisco Xavier*, following the same route, was likely wrecked on the Oregon coast in 1707, an event that is remembered in Tillamook oral tradition and is perhaps the first European contact with the Northwest Coast.

After harassing Spanish treasure ships off the coasts of Peru and Mexico, Sir Francis Drake harbored in a coastal bay probably near San Francisco in 1579, where he made contact with the local Miwok population before returning to England. He named the area Nova Albion (New England) and claimed it for the British Crown.

The first permanent European settlement was established in 1769 in San Diego by Father Junipero Serra and Gaspar de Portolá. Over the next fifty years, the Spanish established twenty-one missions along the coast. Many of these provided the nucleus for the modern cities that exist there today and most retain some vestige of their original mission names. Little survives from the Native arts of this period, since much of it was fragile basketry and feather work. A few examples of remarkable baskets made by Indians associated with the Spanish Missions are known. These are of remarkable quality and incorporate Spanish arms and dedicatory inscriptions.

In the north, contact was much later. A Russian expedition led by Danish mariner Vitus Bering touched Alaska in 1728 and returned in 1741. Eskimo artifacts collected during the second voyage are housed in the Kunstkamera Museum in St. Petersburg. In 1774, Juan Pérez landed on the Alexander Archipelago and exchanged artifacts with the Haida people he encountered there. The following year, another Spanish expedition, led by Bruno de Hezeta, documented the Tlingit. In 1778, James Cook made landfall on Vancouver Island and sailed north to the Bering Strait, still in search of the Northwest Passage. Ignacio de Arteaga followed in 1779 and touched Eskimo territory. The first Western settlement in Alaska was established by Russia in 1784 at Three Saints Bay, near present-day Kodiak, and was followed by an English outpost founded by John Meares at Nootka in 1789, which was seized by Spain, nearly resulting in a war between the countries. A great deal of Northwest Coast art collected by early Spanish expeditions today resides in the Museo de América in Madrid. Some of Cook's material was presented to Sir Hans Sloan, founder of the British Museum, where it still resides.

Following John Gray, who had claimed the area for the United States in 1792, Meriwether Lewis and William Clark navigated down the Columbia River to the Pacific in 1805, having crossed the North American continent. Much of the Native American cultural material they collected is preserved in the Peabody Museum of Archaeology and Ethnology at Harvard University, although the documentation has become muddled and only a handful of objects can be clearly identified with the expedition.

Reliquary Figure, *Eyima Bieri.* **Fang, southern Cameroon/northern Gabon.** Gift of Erle Loran to the Fine Arts Museums of San Francisco (1993.102).

Tribal Arts Guide – WESTERN NORTH AMERICA

Mission San Francisco de Asís, founded in 1776 by Father Francisco Palóu.
Albumen print, 1856.
Photo courtesy of the San Francisco Public Library.

The discovery of gold in the foothills of the Sierra Nevada Mountains in 1848 was the linchpin of change on the western seaboard. Hundreds of thousands of "argonauts" flooded into sparsely populated California, sweeping aside the Native population and the Spanish-descended *Californios* alike in their search for gold. United States statehood for California came in 1850. Oregon followed in 1859, the same year the US purchased Alaska from Russia.

Fast-growing cities were an immediate byproduct of the vast population shift to the West Coast in the mid-nineteenth century. Little thought was given to arts and culture in the first years and indeed the coast's oldest museum, the California Academy of Sciences in San Francisco, was founded in 1853 to address environmental issues relating to gold mining. It quickly amassed a diverse collection that included ethnographic and archaeological specimens, nearly all of which were destroyed in the 1906 earthquake. As decades passed and settlement became more established, western cities sought to curry legitimacy in the eyes of the world by holding massive cultural expositions, and several major museums grew from the collections formed for such fairs. These include The Portland Art Museum (1892), San Francisco's de Young (1895), and the San Diego Museum of Man (1915). Others, such as the Burke Museum (1885), the Cantor Arts Center (1894), and the Phoebe Hearst Museum (1901), were associated with universities. Some of the oldest roots for Western Seaboard museums are in the north, including the Royal British Columbia Museum (1886), Sitka's Sheldon Jackson Museum (1887), and the Vancouver Museum (1894). Not surprisingly, all of these institutions have substantial Native American art holdings that are often regionally weighted, but most also have well-rounded and often world-class collections of art from around the globe. A century or more of assiduous institutional collecting has frequently been augmented by generous patronage that allows entire private collections to be displayed. Stellar examples include the Proctor Stafford Pre-Columbian Collection at the Los Angeles County Museum of Art, the Walter and Marianne Koerner Collection of Native American art at the University of British Columbia, and, most recently, the astonishing Marcia and John Friede Jolika Collection of New Guinea art at the de Young in San Francisco.

Although the institutions of western North America were late entrants in world art collecting, they possess a wealth of treasures from Africa, Oceania, and the Americas that are not to be found elsewhere. An active community of collectors and a cadre of discerning art dealers ensure that these collections are continually growing in scale and importance.

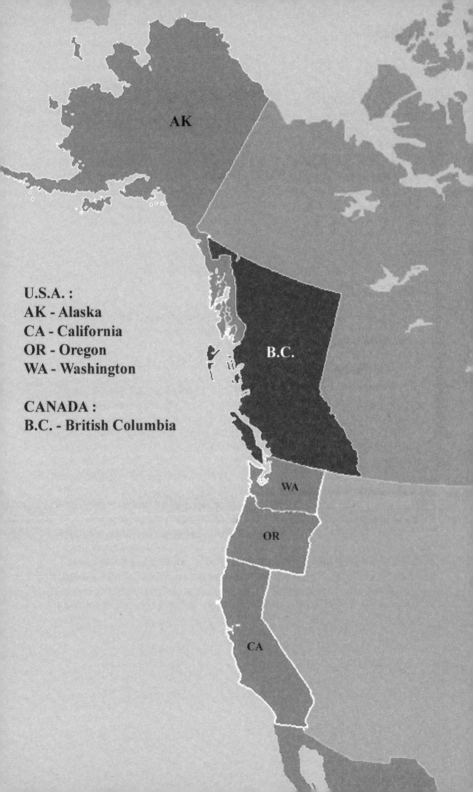

AK

B.C.

U.S.A. :
AK - Alaska
CA - California
OR - Oregon
WA - Washington

CANADA :
B.C. - British Columbia

WA

OR

CA

Simon Paneak Memorial Museum

341 Mekiana Rd.
Anaktuvuk Pass, AK 99721
Phone: 907-661-3413
Fax: 907-661-3414
E-mail: grant.spearman@north-slope.org

☉ **Monday – Friday, 8:30 a.m. – 5 p.m.**
Open limited hours on weekends.
In summer, hours are coincident with
tour flights.

The Simon Paneak Memorial Museum opened in 1986 and contains roughly 200 Nunamiut Inupiat objects from the North Central Brooks Range of Northern Alaska. The pieces, including a caribou skin tent and traditional clothing, were obtained through donations by visiting scientists and local residents. Some items are on loan from other museums. Most of the pieces are on display and storage is accessible to qualified researchers.

Alaska Heritage Museum at Wells Fargo

301 West Northern Lights Blvd.
Anchorage, AK 99503
Phone: 907-265-2834
Fax: 907-265-2860
E-mail: bonadear@wellsfargo.com

☉ **Summer: noon – 5 p.m.**
Winter: noon – 4 p.m.

Founded in 1968, the Alaska Heritage Museum's collection of Alaska Native artifacts is one of the most impressive displays in the Anchorage area. The collection contains a wide range of traditional and contemporary Alaska Native artifacts, including household utensils, articles of clothing, and hunting weapons. The basket collection is especially strong and an extensive collection of contemporary ivory carvings is also on view.

The museum displays over 900 artifacts from a spectrum of Alaska Native cultures including Inupiq, Siberian Yup'ik, Cup'ik, Yup'ik, Alutiiq, Aleut, Athabaskan, Tlingit, and Haida. A collection of Okvik figures and Haida argillite carvings are a special feature of the display.

The objects in the Alaska Heritage Museum were acquired by the National Bank of Alaska under the direction of the Rasmuson family, who owned the bank for three generations. Beginning in the mid 1960s, Elmer Rasmuson and his son, Edward, oversaw the acquisition of the collection. The entirety was sold in a bank merger with Wells Fargo in 2000. The collection is presently displayed in a Wells Fargo branch, which also houses the museum's reference library of some 2,500 volumes.

Anchorage Museum of History and Art

121 W. 7th Ave
Anchorage, AK 99501
Phone: 907-343-6173
Fax: 907-343-6149
E-mail: museum@AnchorageMuseum.org
URL: www.anchoragemuseum.org

☉ September 16 – May 14: Wednesday – Saturday, 10 a.m. – 6 p.m.; Sundays, noon – 5 p.m. Closed Mondays and Tuesdays.
May 15 – September 15: open daily, 9 a.m. – 6 p.m. and until 9 p.m. on Thursdays.

The Anchorage Museum of History & Art began as a public-private partnership to celebrate the 100th anniversary of the 1868 purchase of Alaska from Russia by the United States. A grant from the National Endowment for the Arts enabled the museum to host its first national traveling exhibition, *The Far North*, from the National Gallery of Art in 1973. That same year, the museum became the first in Alaska to be accredited by the American Association of Museums. The Anchorage Museum's collections further its mission to collect, preserve, exhibit, and interpret cultural materials that illustrate the art and history of Alaska and the circumpolar North.

The largest component of the museum's collections is its Alaska Native collections. A major element of this section is composed of large collections of Eskimo and Aleut material that were donated to the Cook Inlet Historical Society in 1955 by Col. Marvin "Muktuk" Marston, Robert Reeve, and Arthur Eide. The historical society's collections became the core of the Anchorage collection when it opened in 1968. The museum's historical collection contains material from the American period of Alaska's history. This includes important collections of clothes and toys, but most of this collection illustrates Alaska's mining, trapping, fishing, oil industry, railroads, and military history.

The tribal collection includes approximately 16,500 pieces of Alaska and Arctic material ranging from prehistoric archaeological objects to contemporary Eskimo ivory carving, Eskimo baskets, Northern Northwest Coast Indian baskets, Eskimo drawings, and Eskimo dolls. Important pieces include a nineteenth century Alutiiq decorated spruce root hat (co-owned with the Alutiiq Museum of Kodiak) and an Aleut/Unangan decorated sea mammal gut cape. The collection also features an archive of 350,000 historic photographs.

The arts of Africa and pre-Columbian, Central American, and North American Native populations are represented by about 750 pieces.

In 1992, the museum became the home to the first regional office of the Smithsonian Institution's National Museum of Natural History Arctic Studies Center. It is currently planning a major expansion in this area.

About ten percent of the Alaskan collection is on view at any given time. Items in storage can be viewed at the request of the public.

Alaska

University of Alaska Museum of the North

University of Alaska Fairbanks
907 Yukon Drive
Fairbanks, AK 99775
Phone: 907-474-7505
Fax: 907-474-5469
E-mail: museum@uaf.edu
URL: www.uaf.edu/museum

⊙ May 15 – September 15:
Daily, 9 a.m. – 7 p.m.
September 16 – May 14: Weekdays, 9
a.m. – 5 p.m.; Weekends, noon – 5 p.m.

In 1926, University of Alaska President Charles Bunnell commissioned Otto William Geist to form a collection of archaeological and paleontological specimens. These materials became the foundation of the University of Alaska Museum of the North collection and were first displayed in 1929.

The archaeology collection contains specimens of prehistoric and historic cultures from throughout Alaska, as well as comparative collections from cultures outside the state. It consists of more than 800,000 artifacts, representing sites dating from 11,000+ BP to the twentieth century, and provides an internationally recognized research base for the entire range of human occupation of the Arctic. The ethnology collection contains over 10,000 objects made and used by Alaska Natives (primarily Inupiaq and Yup'ik Eskimos, Northwest Coast and Athabascan Indians, and Aleuts) from the 1890s to the present. There are exceptional examples of basketry, beadwork, ivory carvings, masks, dolls, and gear used in subsistence activities. It also contains traditional objects from Africa, Oceania, Indonesia, the pre-Columbian Americas, and historic Native America.

In 1980, a facility was built specifically for the museum to function as a research and teaching center. A major expansion is currently underway, which will double its size. The material on display represents highlights from the collections, and the reserve collection is available to qualified researchers.

Pratt Museum

3779 Bartlett Street
Homer, AK 99603
Phone: 907-235-8635 ext. 38
Fax: 907-235-2764
E-mail: info@prattmuseum.org
URL: www.prattmuseum.org

⊙ Mid-May through mid-September:
Daily, 10 a.m. – 6 p.m.
Mid-September through mid-May:
Tuesday – Sunday, noon – 5 p.m.
Closed Monday. Closed the month of
January, Thanksgiving Day, Christmas
Day, and New Year's Day.

The Pratt Museum is located on the shores of Kachemak Bay on the southeast part of Cook Inlet. Its anthropology collection consists of 9,741 objects. Its archaeological artifacts were excavated from local sites and form a well-documented research collection of the earliest-known human inhabitants of Kachemak Bay, ranging from the Ocean Bay Culture (4500 years BP) to the Kachemak Tradition to the prehistoric Dena'ina Athabaskans (c. AD 1400). Ethnographic artifacts include basketry, dolls, fishing and hunting implements, boats, household tools, clothing, and ornamental objects representing the three major regional Native Alaskan coastal cultures, the Dena'ina Athabaskan, Pacific Eskimo, and Aleut. One of the rarest artifacts is a well-preserved 1,000-year-old Kachemak Tradition birch bark basket that miraculously survived in a tide-swept cliff. The museum is recognized by the Kenaitze Indian Tribe of Dena'ina Athabaskans as a regional repository for cultural materials and cares for their repatriated counting cords and newly excavated archaeological materials from the Upper Russian River.

The museum's research collection includes 29,545 objects plus an extensive library, media collection, and archives. The collections constitute a regionally distinctive resource for research, exhibition, and educational use.

Most of the objects were field collected by the Pratt Museum. About five percent of the collection is on exhibit. Collections in storage are accessible for researchers and qualified users.

Alaska State Museum

395 Whittier St.
Juneau, AK 99801-1718
Phone: 907-465-2901
Fax: 907-465-2976
URL: www.museums.state.ak.us

☉ **May 16 through mid-September: daily, 8:30 a.m. – 5:30 p.m. Closed May 30, July 4, Sept. 5. Mid-September to mid-May: Tuesday – Saturday, 10 a.m. – 4 p.m. Closed holidays.**

The Alaska State Museum was established on June 6, 1900, when an Act of Congress created the Historical Library and Museum for the Territory of Alaska. The Alaska State Museum was first accredited by the American Association of Museums in 1975.

The collections of the Alaska State Museum (which are shared by the facility in Juneau and the Sheldon Jackson Museum in Sitka) represent the diverse cultures and rich historical record of a large geographic area. Of the museum's more than 27,000 cataloged objects, Alaskan Native material—including Alaskan Eskimo, Athabascan, Aleut, and Northwest Coast groups—dominates the collection. Items from daily life as well as ceremonial and sacred objects are well represented. The collection of Northwest Coast and Eskimo baskets is among the most comprehensive in existence and includes fragments of three recently discovered baskets which have been dated to 5000 years BP, the oldest ever recovered in Alaska or the Northwest Coast. The collection of Eskimo carved ivory is comprehensive and ranges from prehistoric to twentieth century. The museum also maintains an outstanding collection of work by contemporary Native artists.

The natural history collection contains approximately 1,200 seashells, minerals, skeletons, fossils, and mounted animals and birds.

The two State Museum facilities have an extensive collection, about eighty-five percent of which is not on permanent exhibit. Many of the artifacts in storage are available for research or loan.

Alaska

Tongass Historical Museum

629 Dock St.
Ketchikan, AK 99901
URL: www.city.ketchikan.ak.us/depart-
ments/museums/tongass.html

☺ May – September:
Daily, 8 a.m. – 5 p.m.
October – April:
Wednesday – Friday, 1 p.m. – 5 p.m.;
Saturday, 10 a.m. – 4 p.m.; Sunday,
1 p.m. – 4 p.m. Closed Monday &
Tuesday.

The Tongass Historical Museum collects, preserves, and interprets material and information pertaining to the history, art, and culture of Ketchikan and Southeast Alaska. The museum features permanent and temporary exhibits based on its own collections and community participation. It also hosts traveling exhibitions from other institutions and offers public programs, special events, workshops, and educational programs that relate to Ketchikan area history. The museum's extensive historical archive and photograph collections are available for research.

Totem Heritage Center

601 Deermount
Ketchikan, AK 99901
URL: www.city.ketchikan.ak.us/depart-
ments/museums/totem.html

☺ May – September:
Daily, 8 a.m. – 5 p.m.
October – April:
Monday – Friday, 1 p.m. – 5 p.m. Closed
Saturday and Sunday.

The Totem Heritage Center was established in 1976 to preserve endangered nineteenth century totem poles retrieved from uninhabited Tlingit and Haida village sites near Ketchikan. The magnificent, original poles are displayed at the center in conjunction with other totems and Native Alaskan artifacts. In addition to functioning as a museum, the Totem Heritage Center also preserves and promotes the traditional arts and crafts of the Tlingit, Haida, and Tsimshian cultures through a nationally recognized program of Native arts classes and other activities.

Alutiiq Museum and Archaeological Repository

215 Mission Road, Suite 101
Kodiak, AK 99615
Phone: 907-486-7004
Fax: 907-486-7048
E-mail: receptionist@alutiiqmuseum.com
URL: www.alutiiqmuseum.com

☉ Labor Day – Memorial Day:
Wednesday – Friday, 9 a.m. – 5 p.m.;
Saturday, 10:30 a.m. – 4:30 p.m.
Memorial Day – Labor Day:
Monday – Friday, 9 a.m. – 5 p.m.;
Saturday, 10 a.m. – 5 p.m.

The Alutiiq Museum opened in 1995 and its collection highlights the Alutiiq, a Pacific Eskimo people who have inhabited the Kodiak Archipelago, Kenai Peninsula, and Alaska Peninsula for more than 7,500 years.

The museum is an outgrowth of the cultural programs of the Kodiak Area Native Association. Upon its opening, it received more than 100,000 items from that organization for its collection. Additions to the collections have been made by other Alutiiq corporations and tribal councils, and from excavations performed by the museum and other institutions and universities.

Objects of note include a group of artifacts from Larsen Bay (which was the first collection to be reparitated from the Smithsonian Institution under NAGPRA) and Karluk One, a collection that includes remarkably well-preserved wood artifacts from AD 1500–1800.

The permanent display collection represents about one percent of the museum's holdings.

Sheldon Jackson Museum

104 College Drive
Sitka, AK 99835
Phone: 907-747-8981
Fax: 907-747-3004
URL: www.museums.state.ak.us

☉ May 15 – September 15:
Daily, 9 a.m. – 5 p.m.
September 16 – May 14: **Tuesday –**
Saturday, 10 a.m. – 4 p.m.

This museum was founded in 1887 by the Reverend Doctor Sheldon Jackson and the Alaska Society of Natural History and Ethnology. The octagonal structure that now houses the collection is notable for being the first concrete building in Alaska. The majority of its 5,800 Alaska Native objects were acquired between 1888–1898 by Jackson with the assistance of teachers, missionaries, members of the Alaska Society of Natural History and Ethnology, and members of the Native community. As General Agent for Education for the US Bureau of Education, Jackson traveled throughout the region. As he did so, he purchased or traded for objects in the areas he visited. Highlights of the collection include Inupiat and Yup'ik Eskimo watercraft, clothing, masks, tools, and equipment of daily life. Tlingit regalia, including the raven helmet worn by K'alyaan during the Battle of 1804 as the Tlingit defended their homeland against the Russians, is a prominent part of the collection. Haida argillite carvings, Athabascan canoes and Aleut/Alutiiq masks are also held by the museum.

About 32% of the collection is on exhibit. The museum is part of the Alaska State Museums system, which has another facility in Juneau.

Alaska

The Bancroft Library

University of California
Berkeley, CA 94720-6000
Tel: 510-642-6481
URL: bancroft.berkeley.edu

☺ **Monday – Friday, 10 a.m. – 5 p.m.**
Closed major holidays.

The Bancroft Library is the primary special collections library at the University of California, Berkeley. One of the largest and most heavily used libraries of manuscripts, rare books, and unique materials in the United States, it holds more 600,000 volumes; 60,000,000 manuscript items; 2,800,000 photographs/pictorial materials; and 23,000 maps. It is a vast resource for the study of ethnology, particularly relating to Native California and pre-Columbian Mexico.

Phoebe Apperson Hearst Museum of Anthropology

University of California Berkeley
2200 University Ave.
Berkeley, CA 94720
102 Kroeber Hall
Phone: 510-642-3682
Fax: 510-642-6271
E-mail: pahma@berkeley.edu
URL: hearstmuseum.berkeley.edu

☺ **Wednesday – Saturday, 10 a.m. –**
4:30 p.m.; Sunday, noon – 4 p.m.

The Phoebe Apperson Hearst Museum of Anthropology, formerly the Lowie Museum of Anthropology, was founded in 1901 as the first anthropology museum west of the Mississippi. Its major patron, Phoebe Hearst, supported systematic collecting efforts by both archaeologists and ethnologists to provide the University of California with the materials for a museum to support a major department of anthropology. The museum's collections have grown from an initial nucleus of approximately 230,000 objects gathered under the Hearst's patronage to an estimated 3.8 million items.

Archaeologists Max Uhle and George Reisner are two important early figures in the museum. Their archaeological expeditions in Peru and Egypt resulted in major collections, which the museum continues to hold. The museum also holds important collections from Alaska and British Columbia, as well as from cultures around the world. The most extensive collection is of California Native material, which is the world's largest and most comprehensive. It was begun by Philip M. Jones and expanded by Alfred M. Kroeber and others in the early twentieth century. The museum may be best remembered by the public from when it was physically housed in San Francisco (1903–1931), during which time a key attraction was Ishi, the last member of the Native California Yahi group. He lived at the museum from 1911 until his death in 1916 and worked with anthropologists to document the ways of his people.

Since 1931, the museum has been housed in small quarters on the university campus with only a tiny part of its collection on public display. It grants access to its materials in storage for the purpose of research and study conforming to appropriate standards of scholarly discipline, and to individual scholars and members of groups whose traditional culture is represented by collections held by the museum.

California

Picard Trade Bead Museum

27885 Berwick Drive
Carmel, CA 93923
Phone: 831-625-7108
Fax: 831-626-4172
E-mail: info@picardbeads.com
URL: www.picardbeads.com

☺ **By appointment.**

The Picard Museum was founded in 1996 and displays over 100,000 glass, metal, stone, and shell beads used for trade in Africa, as well as some 500 assorted African objects and textiles. A donation by the Societa Veneziana Conterie of Murano, Italy, provided antique sample cards of Venetian beads, which provide additional context for the collection.

Chico Museum

141 Salem Street
Chico, CA 95928
Phone: 530-891-4336
E-mail: chicomuseum@chico.com.
URL: www.chicomuseum.org

☺ **Wednesday – Sunday, noon – 4 p.m.**

Housed in the former Carnegie Library Building in downtown Chico, the Chico Museum has hosted more than eighty-five exhibits celebrating the distinct heritage of the city since it opened in February 1986. The museum's two main galleries feature changing exhibits focusing on aspects of Chico's past and present. The museum also houses Chico's Chinese Taoist temple, which features altars and original artifacts. Planned enhancements to the installation include exhibits on Chico's Mechoopda Maidu Indians.

Petterson Museum

730 Plymouth Rd.
Claremont, CA 91711
Phone: 909-399-5544
Fax: 909-399-5508
URL: pilgrimplace.org/asp/Site/OurServices/P
ettersonMuseum/view.asp

☺ **Friday – Sunday, 2 p.m. – 4 p.m.; and by appointment.**

The Petterson Museum was founded in 1968 and contains roughly 3,500 tribal objects and over 10,000 works of fine art, folk art, and material culture from around the world. Acquired through individual donors, the collection includes basketry, textiles, sculpture, beadwork, ceramics, metalwork, paintings, costumes, and dolls from every continent.

Richard & Alice Petterson were significant donors, as were many former residents of Pilgrim Place, the complex in which the museum is housed. This is a community for retired church workers, missionaries, and their families, which was formed in 1915.

Noteworthy displays include a collection of tapa cloths from Micronesia and Polynesia; Mayan clothing from Guatemala; West African sculpture; pre-Columbian ceramics; and historic and contemporary pieces from Mexico and Central America.

Pomona College Museum of Art, Montgomery Art Center

333 N. College Way
Claremont, CA 91711-6344
Phone: 909-621-8283
Fax: 909-621-8989
E-mail: steven.comba@pomona.edu

☉ Tuesday – Friday, noon – 5 p.m.;
Saturday and Sunday, 1 p.m. – 5 p.m.
Closed Monday.

The fine art collections of Pomona College are housed in the Pomona College Museum of Art. The museum is located in the Montgomery Art Center, which was inaugurated in 1958 and named for the late Gladys K. Montgomery, a Pomona trustee and Los Angeles civic leader. Among important holdings are the Kress Collection of fifteenth- and sixteenth-century Italian panel paintings and more than 5,000 examples of pre-Columbian to twentieth-century American Indian art and artifacts, which have been assembled over the last seventy years. This collection is particularly rich in Californian and Southwestern basketry, Southwestern ceramics (both pre-Columbian and historic), and beadwork of the Plains and Great Lakes.

The Pomona collection of Native American art owes its existence to Robert J. Bernard, who was active with the college from 1917–1963, when he retired as president. In 1929 he persuaded Mr. and Mrs. Jonathan Tibbet to donate their collection of Native American art to the college. Other major donations followed, including that of Emil P. Steffa, a Pomona alumnus (class of 1899) whose meticulously documented collection of California Indian baskets has lasting historical importance.

Ruth Chandler Williamson Gallery, Scripps College

1030 Columbia Avenue
Claremont, CA 91711
Phone: 909-607-3397
Fax: 909-607-4691
E-mail: kirk.delman@scrippscollege.edu
URL: www.scrippscollege.edu/dept/gallery

☉ Wednesday – Sunday, 1 p.m. –
5 p.m., during exhibitions.
Closed Monday and Tuesday.

Founded in 1935, The Ruth Chandler Williamson Gallery at Scripps College has a permanent collection of approximately 7,500 art objects, which span 3,000 years and the majority of the world's cultures. Objects from the collection are used in classes for teaching purposes, displayed in campus exhibitions, and loaned to other institutions for exhibition worldwide.

The current building, which opened in 1993, houses African sculpture and masks that are mostly tourist objects as well as 194 authentic pre-Columbian and Native American pottery objects, largely from the collection of Edward Nagel. None of the tribal and pre-Columbian objects are on permanent display, but they can be viewed by appointment.

Heritage of the Americas Museum

Cuyamaca College
2110 Cuyamaca College Drive West
El Cajon, CA 92019
Phone: 619-670-5194
URL: www.cuyamaca.net/museum

☉ Tuesday – Friday, 10 a.m. – 4 p.m.;
Saturday, noon – 4 p.m.
**Closed Sunday, Monday, and selected
holidays.**

The Heritage of the Americas Museum, located on the campus of Cuyamaca
College in El Cajon, is an educational and cultural center featuring the natural history and prehistoric and historic art and culture of the Americas. The building is
divided into five wings, each addressing a different aspect of the history of the
Americas.

The archaeology wing features about 10,000 archaic ceremonial and projectile
points that are artistically displayed on a geological time clock. Some date as
early as the paleolithic period.

Another part of the display addresses the pre-Columbian cultures of Central and
South America. The Maya are particularly well represented, as are the cultures of
ancient Peru.

Tribal cultures of the Americas are represented with displays of pipes, pottery,
stone axes and decorative beads and ornaments. The installation of more than
200 objects also features eagle feathered headdresses and dance regalia along
with buckskin clothing and accessories, moccasins, breast plates, a dentalium col-
lared dress, and a baby carrier. A particularly important piece is the buffalo hide
council robe of Cheyenne Chief Thunderbird.

The museum's collection also features more than 500 necklaces formed from
beads of jade, stone, ivory, shell, gold, silver, copper and pottery, and ranging in
age from 600 BC–AD 1200.

There is also a display representing Pacific Island cultures and their possible
although speculative relationship to the Native cultures of the Americas.

SANA Art Foundation

131 S. Orange Street
Escondido, CA 92025
(Located on Orange between West Grand
and 2nd Avenue)
Phone: 760-737-2903
Fax: 760-737-2903
E-mail: artfoundations@hotmail.com

☉ **Hours are event-driven and by appointment.**

The SANA Art Foundation is a non profit organization that was founded by Edward and Mina Smith in 1996. In 2004, work began on a new location in Escondido and the new building now provides educational programs that relate to the historical and evolving culture of Native American, African, and Oceanic peoples. The foundation has a collection of over 1,000 objects from South and East Africa, as well as more than 1,000 objects from elsewhere in Africa, Oceania and Americas. The library has over 2,000 books and periodicals on non-Western art.

A significant portion of the foundation's South and East African art collection originates from the former Prynnesberg Museum, a privately owned collection formed by Charles Newberry in the late nineteenth century. Beadwork, wood and ceramic vessels, headrests, staffs, statues, puppets, and wirework make up most of the artifact collection.

A Blackfoot war shirt, c.1880, from the Northern Plains is also of particular interest, as is an Oceanic tapa/kapa collection of bark cloth and a nineteenth century Tolei Mask.

Fresno Art Museum

2233 N. First Street
Fresno, CA 93703
Phone: 559-441-4221
Fax: 559-441-4227
URL: www.fresnoartmuseum.org

☉ **Tuesday – Sunday, 11 a.m. – 5 p.m.**
Thursday open until 8 p.m.
Closed on Mondays, Thanksgiving,
Christmas and New Year's Day.

The Fresno Art Museum collects, preserves, and exhibits to the public tangible objects valuable to art and history. Since its inception as a regional arts center in 1948, the museum has grown into an important center for contemporary and modern art. Originally called the Fresno Art Center and Museum, it changed its name to the Fresno Art Museum in the late 1980s.

In addition to its wide range of contemporary and modern works by local, national, and international artists, the museum has an impressive display of Mexican art from pre-Columbian times to the present. The planned bequest of significant collections of pre-Columbian ceramics will further the museum's mission as both an educational facility and a repository for important collections from the Central Valley.

California

Antelope Valley Indian Museum State Historic Park

5701 East Avenue M
Lancaster, CA 93535
Phone: 661-946-3055
URL: www.avim.parks.ca.gov.

☉ Mid-September to mid-June:
Weekends only, 11 a.m. – 4 p.m.
Prearranged guided tours Tuesdays and
Thursdays, from 10 a.m. – noon, for
school groups and for adult groups of
10 or more. Closed during the summer.

Built in the 1920s among towering rock formations in the Mojave Desert, this museum is an eclectic folk art structure that exhibits and interprets a large collection of unique artifacts, with a focus on the prehistoric and contemporary American Indian cultures of the western Great Basin, California, and the Southwest. Founder Howard Arden Edwards was an ardent admirer of American Indian cultures and had amassed a sizeable collection of artifacts, which he exhibited in the building he constructed and lived in. In 1940, Edwards sold the property to Grace Oliver, who expanded the museum collections and converted the entire building to display the material. The State of California took control of the museum in 1979.

The museum's collections include basketry, textiles (including a collection of Navajo rugs acquired in the 1920s and a Hopi wearing robe from the 1860s), pottery, and stone artifacts from the Southwest; cultural materials of various types from the Great Basin; and a variety of materials representing California American Indian groups. The largest single collection is from the Chumash and Tongva peoples of the California coast and Channel Islands. The museum's catalogued holdings number approximately 7,500 artifacts. Approximately half of the collection is on display in an open exhibit.

San Joaquin County Historical Museum

11793 N Micke Grove Road
Lodi, CA 95240
Phone: 209-331-2055
Fax: 209-331-2057
E-mail: info@sanjoaquinhistory.org
URL: www.sanjoaquinhistory.org

☉ **Wednesday – Sunday, 10 a.m. –**
3 p.m.
Closed Mondays, Tuesdays, and major
holidays.

The San Joaquin County Historical Museum is located outside of Lodi, California. It was established in 1966 through an agreement between the County of San Joaquin and the San Joaquin County Historical Society. The collections have grown from a few hundred items from the estate of William G. and Julia Harrison Micke to over 50,000 items representative of the development of San Joaquin County agriculture and history. The museum was accredited by the American Association of Museums in 1973.

The museum holds a collection of artifacts from the Yokuts and Miwok peoples, who were native to the San Joaquin region. It also has the tribal and pre-Columbian collection of Stockton lawyer Joseph C. Tope.

California African American Museum

600 State Drive, Exposition Park
Los Angeles, CA 90037
Phone: 213-744-7432
Fax: 213-744-2050
E-mail: info@caamuseum.org
URL: www.caamuseum.org

☉ **Wednesday – Saturday, 10 a.m. – 4 p.m.; first Sunday of the month, 11 a.m. – 6 p.m.**

Chartered by the State of California in 1977, the California African American Museum was founded as the California Museum of Afro-American History and Culture. The current facility was opened for the Los Angeles Summer Olympic Games in 1984. In 2001 the museum temporarily closed its exhibition facilities for major infrastructure renovations and reopened in March 2003.

The museum focuses on African-American history, but it holds approximately 400 objects of traditional African sculpture. Nearly all were acquired through private donations from a variety of sources, including Cathryn M. Jones.

Most of the objects are masks, sculptures, and textiles from West and Central Africa. About twenty are on display and most of the rest are stored on-site and are accessible by appointment to qualified researchers.

Autry National Center
Museum of the American West

4700 Western Heritage Way
Los Angeles, CA 90027-1462
Phone: 323-667-2000
Fax: 323-660-5721
URL: www.museumoftheamericanwest.org

☉ **Tuesday – Sunday, 10 a.m. – 5 p.m. Closed on most Mondays but open for Martin Luther King Day, Presidents' Day, Memorial Day, and Labor Day. Open Thursday until 8 p.m. with free admission after 4 p.m.**

Performing legend Gene Autry first conceived of this museum as a means of interpreting the American West for the general public. When the museum opened in 1988 as the Autry Museum of Western Heritage, its exhibits were intended to tell the story of the region from prehistory to the present, and each artifact on display was selected to fill a particular role. It also contained memorabilia relating to the life and career of the "Singing Cowboy." Since then, the museum has grown and its focus has evolved. Today the collection numbers more than 78,000 art objects and artifacts from Native American cultures and the western expansion of the United States.

In 2002 the museum merged with the Women of the West Museum in Boulder, Colorado. The following year it also merged with the Southwest Museum of the American Indian in Los Angeles. The Autry changed its name to the Museum of the American West with the governing organization of all three museums being the Autry National Center. Today, the three museums and the center's Institute for the Study of the American West provide different lenses, curatorial specializations, and distinctive lines of intellectual inquiry to delve into the multifaceted study of the American West.

Los Angeles County Museum of Art

5905 Wilshire Blvd.
Los Angeles, CA 90036
Phone: 323-857-6000
URL: www.lacma.org

☉ **LACMA: Monday, Tuesday, Thursday: noon – 8 p.m.; Friday: noon – 9 p.m.; Saturday, Sunday: 11 a.m. – 8 p.m.**

LACMA West: Monday, Tuesday, Thursday, Friday: noon – 5 p.m.; Saturday, Sunday: 11 a.m. – 5 p.m.;

Closed Wednesdays, Thanksgiving, and Christmas day.

The Los Angeles County Museum of Art is the central museum for the greater Los Angeles region. LACMA was founded in 1910 as part of the Museum of Science, History and Art in the Exposition Park area near the University of Southern California, and became an independent art-focused institution in 1961. The museum moved to its current location in 1965. It has major collections relating to all aspects of Western and world art.

Among its many holdings is one of the most important collections of pre-Columbian art in the United States. The collection is particularly strong in objects from the major civilizations of ancient Mexico. A significant portion, which was assembled by Proctor Stafford and acquired by the museum in 1986, represents the ceramic funerary offerings found in the tombs of the west Mexican states of Nayarit, Colima, and Jalisco. The museum's Constance McCormick Fearing Collection contains a broad selection of ceramic sculpture from West Mexico as well as from other areas of Mesoamerica. Finely carved stone sculpture forms an important component of the Fearing collection, ranging from the exquisite jade figures produced by Olmec artists on the Gulf Coast to the massive and intricately designed basalt representation of ball game regalia from Veracruz.

The ancient kingdoms of Peru are also well represented in the galleries. The collection features an array of intricately patterned textiles, brilliantly painted ceramics, and finely worked metal objects spanning the geographical breadth and temporal history of this great region.

The museum has a costume and textile department that oversees a large collection of clothing, textiles, and accessories ranging from the pre-Columbian Americas to contemporary couture. The department has outstanding collections of Islamic, South and Southeast Asian, and Far Eastern material. It has a strong collection of Indonesian textiles, as well as significant Chinese, Japanese, Tibetan, and Korean holdings.

The Southeast Asian Art Gallery displays works from Burma, Cambodia, Indonesia, Laos, Sri Lanka, Thailand, and Vietnam. Bronze and Iron Age objects from the Dongson culture of Indonesia and Vietnam and the Ban Chiang culture of Thailand are on view along with Buddhist and Hindu sculpture from all periods and regions. The collection of Sri Lankan art is one of the largest and most comprehensive outside Asia.

Los Angeles County Museum of Natural History

900 Exposition Blvd.
Los Angeles, CA 90007
Phone: 213-763-DINO
URL: www.nhm.org

☉ **Monday – Friday, 9:30 a.m. – 5 p.m.; Saturday, Sunday and some holidays, 10 a.m. – 5 p.m. Closed Independence Day, Thanksgiving Day, Christmas Day, and New Year's Day.**

The Natural History Museum of Los Angeles County is the second oldest cultural institution in Los Angeles, having opened its doors in 1913. It is the largest natural and historical museum in the Western United States, safeguarding more than 33 million diverse specimens and artifacts.

Three floors of exhibits address a wide variety of historical and scientific topics. Amidst the formidable dinosaurs and taxidermy, Native American and pre-Columbian cultures, and historical artifacts from California and Southwest history are well represented.

The Times Mirror Hall of Native American Cultures showcases more than 800 pieces from the museum's permanent collections in sixteen different interpretive areas. Highlights include Navajo textiles from the William Randolph Hearst Collection, California and Great Basin baskets, Southwest pottery and jewelry, Plains beadwork, and replicas of a two-story Pueblo cliff dwelling and a collector's California Craftsman house (the latter featuring Native American art, which was popular for decorating at the time). One exhibit case features ninety-nine of the 3,951 Southwest fetish carvings donated by Dr. and Mrs. Boyd W. Walker in 1997. Together they reflect the dynamic and diverse artistic skills of Native American peoples of the American Southwest, who have carved small animals from stone and shell since ancient times.

The Ancient Latin America Hall covers an array of prehistoric societies of Latin America, including the Maya, Aztec, Inca, and many other cultural groups. Ceramic vessels, figurines, personal adornment items, and other artifacts from Mexico and Central and South America are on permanent display.

The Lando Hall of California History examines the Southwest beginning in the sixteenth century and traces its evolution through time and place to downtown Los Angeles in 1940. The gallery is organized chronologically and features twelve themes: Native Americans; New World Exploration; Spanish Outpost; International Competition; Mexican Territory; War with the U.S.; 31st State; Craftsman Style; Agriculture; Land, Sea & Air; Motion Pictures; and City of Los Angeles. In this hall the history of the past appears in both artifacts and the records of the people who lived there.

The museum also holds some 5,000 African objects. Among these are a number of Benin bronzes and a collection of Cameroon Grassfields sculpture that was collected before 1914.

California

Tribal Art Museum Collections in the UNITED STATES

Southwest Museum of the American Indian

234 Museum Drive
Los Angeles, CA 90065
Phone: 323-221-2164
Fax: 323-224-8223
URL: www.southwestmuseum.org

☺ **Tuesday – Sunday, 10 a.m. – 5 p.m.**
Closed on most Mondays.
Open for Martin Luther King Day,
President's Day, Memorial Day, and
Labor Day. Closed Thanksgiving and
Christmas.

The Southwest Museum holds one of the nation's most important museum, library, and archive collections related to Native American art and culture. It also has extensive holdings of pre-Hispanic, Spanish colonial, Latino, and Western American art and artifacts. For nearly one hundred years it has supported research, publications, exhibitions, and other educational activities. A privately funded nonprofit organization and the oldest museum in Los Angeles, the Southwest Museum was founded in 1907 by Charles Fletcher Lummis and members of the Southwest Society. In the 1920s, the museum narrowed its focus to anthropology and its subject matter to the cultural history and prehistory of the indigenous peoples of the Americas. Between 1925 and the mid-1960s, the Southwest Museum sponsored archaeological investigations in Casa Grande, Arizona; the Mimbres area in New Mexico; Mesa House and Gypsum, Nevada; and Twentynine Palms, California, among others.

In 1932, Frederick Webb Hodge became the museum's director. Under Hodge's leadership, the museum's focus expanded to include indigenous peoples living in most areas west of the Mississippi, and its collections grew dramatically. The museum's collections contain more than 350,000 objects including: 11,000 pieces of pottery; 13,000 baskets; 1,000 Kachina dolls; 1,300 Navajo textiles; 600 Pueblo textiles; and beadwork, costumes, clothing, tools, and paintings from the Great Plains, Plateau, and Eastern Woodland Nations. The museum's collections are supported and enhanced by the holdings of the Braun Research Library.

In 2003, after a long and failing battle with finances, the museum elected to merge with the Autry Museum of the American West and came under the directorship of the Autry National Center. This has provided it with the financial base to support its exhibitions and program. It is also documenting its collection, which will be available on the Autry National Center's online database in the near future.

UCLA Fowler Museum of Cultural History

North Campus, UCLA
405 Hilgard Ave.
Los Angeles, CA 90095
Phone: 310-825-4361
Fax: 310-206-7007
E-mail: fowlerws@arts.ucla.edu
URL: www.fowler.ucla.edu

☺ **Wednesday – Sunday, noon – 5 p.m.;**
Thursday until 8 p.m.
Closed Monday and Tuesday.

This important anthropology museum was established in 1963 by then UCLA Chancellor Franklin D. Murphy as the Museum and Laboratories of Ethnic Arts and Technology. A large, state-of-the-art facility opened in fall 1992 and was named for collector and inventor Francis E. Fowler, Jr., whose family was instrumental in making the project possible.

The museum holds approximately 150,000 objects, including an African collection that offers a superb representation of the arts of several African nations including Nigeria, Ghana, Cameroon, Zaire, Kenya, and South Africa. The collection contains a spectacular array of Yoruba beaded objects, including a majestic throne, elaborate chiefly gowns, and sophisticated divination regalia.

Holdings from Indonesia and the Philippines include numerous sculptural works—especially from Sumatra, Borneo, Sulawesi, and Luzon—as well as important collections of baskets from Luzon and plaited mats from Borneo. The museum's collection of betel-chewing paraphernalia, representing several countries in South and Southeast Asia, is considered one of the finest in the world. Other Asian materials include textiles from India and Japan, shadow puppets from throughout the region, and a group of sculpture and textiles from aboriginal Taiwan.

The primary strength of the Oceanic collection lies in materials from Papua New Guinea, especially the Papuan Gulf, Sepik River, Maprik area, and the Massim/Trobriand region. Also included are significant holdings from Aboriginal Australia and Polynesia, including forty-five rare Maori cloaks.

The museum houses approximately 24,700 Latin American objects, including a major collection of Haitian works related to Vodou. Mexican holdings include pre-Columbian, colonial, contemporary folk, and ethnographic collections. Additional objects include traditional art, costume, and textiles from Guatemala and Panama; African-American art and material culture from Brazil and Suriname; objects field collected among the Warao and Yecuana Indians of the Orinoco Delta of Venezuela; and pre-Columbian ceramics and textiles of Peru. Native American materials from the U.S. and Canada are a small but significant part of the collection.

The Sir Henry Wellcome Collection of 30,000 objects, assembled early in the twentieth century by Wellcome and given to the museum in 1965, forms the core of the African and Oceanic holdings and represents the single largest gift. An exceptional collection of more than 900 Mexican works was donated in 1997 by the Daniel Family and includes magnificent ceramic Trees of Life, Day of the Dead figurines, and masks from Metepec, Oaxaca, Michoacan, Jalisco, Puebla, and Guanajuato.

Little of the material is on permanent display, though it appears frequently in the museum's active exhibitions program. Storage is accessible to scholars by written request only.

California

Monterey Museum of Art

559 Pacific Street
Monterey, CA 93940
Phone: 831-372-5477
URL: www.montereyart.org

☉ Wednesday – Saturday, 11 a.m. –
5 p.m.; Sunday 1 p.m. – 4 p.m.

The Monterey Museum of Art's collections, exhibitions, and educational programs reflect the unique cultural heritage of the Central Coast of California and its distinctive influence within the global cultural community.

The museum's permanent collection includes California paintings, sculpture, works on paper, and photography. While it has little tribal art, it does have strong collections of Asian art and international folk art.

Hearst Art Gallery

Saint Mary's College of California
1928 St. Mary's Road
Moraga, CA 94556
Phone: 925-631-4379
Fax: 925-376-5128
URL: gallery.stmarys-ca.edu

☉ Wednesday – Sunday,
11 a.m. – 4:30 p.m.

The campus art gallery at Saint Mary's College was opened in 1934 and was operated by the art faculty until the mid-1970s. The present Hearst Art Gallery was built with the aid of a grant from the Hearst Foundation and opened in 1977.

The museum has a few hundred works of tribal art and pre-Columbian antiquities in its permanent collection. It is actively interested in acquiring more. The gallery presently has no permanent display space for the material, but it has been active over the years in holding special exhibitions relating to tribal art, particularly from Africa.

Marin Museum of the American Indian

2200 Novato Boulevard
Novato, CA 94948
Phone: 415-897-4064
Fax: 415-892-7804
E-Mail: office@marinindian.com
URL: www.marinindian.com

☉ Tuesday – Friday, 10 a.m. – 3 p.m.;
Saturday and Sunday, noon – 4 p.m.

The Marin Museum of the American Indian was founded in 1967 in response to the rapid development of Marin County. Construction activity in the county unearthed masses of archaeological objects related to the early inhabitation of the region by the Coast Miwok peoples. The museum was originally designed to serve as a repository for these materials. Today, the museum still houses a large collection of Coast Miwok artifacts, but its scope has broadened considerably, and its programs and collection represent Native American cultures from across North America. Objects in the collection include Navajo textiles, Eskimo carvings, Plains beadwork, birch bark baskets, and Northwest Coast masks.

Oakland Museum of California

1000 Oak Street
Oakland, CA 94607
Phone: 510-238-2200
URL: www.museumca.org/

☺ **Wednesday – Saturday, 10 a.m. – 5 p.m.; Sunday, noon – 5 p.m.; first Friday of each month until 9 p.m. Closed Mondays, Tuesdays and major holidays.**

The Oakland Museum of California opened in 1969 and is one of the most architecturally interesting museums in the country, a graceful, three-tiered blend of spacious galleries, terraces, patios, sculpture gardens, and ponds.

Comprehensive permanent exhibits on three floors portray California's natural wonders, events, eras, and people who have shaped the state. It also houses fine examples of the art that Californians have produced since artist-explorers first ventured into the Yosemite Valley.

The History Department collections originated with a predecessor institution, the Oakland Public Museum, which opened in 1910. Founding curator Charles P. Wilcomb was a pioneer cultural historian and field ethnographer. He was concerned with documenting the roots of peoples inhabiting California, especially California's Native peoples. More than half of the 6,000 Native American objects in the history collection were either collected by Wilcomb between 1908 and 1915 during collecting expeditions throughout Northern California and British Columbia or given to the museum by donors he cultivated. The collection represents a full range of material culture associated with the region's indigenous peoples, including baskets, dance regalia, clothing, tools, weapons, and raw materials. It includes one of the finest collections of California baskets in the world. Since Wilcomb documented the locations and names of people associated with the artifacts he collected, curators today are sometimes able to connect collection objects with contemporary descendants of Wilcomb's informants.

The History Department also curates Native American objects from regions outside California, including the Arctic, Northwest Coast, Southwest, Plateau and Great Basin, Subarctic, Great Plains, Southern California, and the Eastern United States.

Other highlights of the museum's History Department holdings include extensive collections of Asian and Pacific ethnographic artifacts, costumes, and historical objects. Some of the Pacific material is notable for high artistic achievement but much of it illustrates the diversity of everyday life among Oceanic cultures. Consisting of approximately 3,400 artifacts and photographs collected since 1900, the collection includes approximately 1,098 artifacts from Polynesia, 739 from Melanesia, 484 from Micronesia, 67 from Australia, 488 from the Philippines, and 348 from Indonesia. The 1,028-object Rabe Collection forms the centerpiece of this group. A San Francisco dentist, John Rabe departed around 1887 for tropical climates, where he spent six years traveling to Micronesia, Polynesia, Melanesia, Australia, the Philippines, and Indonesia. The Rabe Collection is notable not only for its breadth and scope, but for the quality of associated documentation—Rabe's notes include detailed information relating to cultural attribution, location, and use of many of the objects.

California

Agua Caliente Cultural Museum

219 S. Palm Canyon Drive
Palm Springs, CA 92262
Phone: 760-778-1079
Fax: 760-322-7724
E-mail: mail@accmuseum.org
URL: www.accmuseum.org

☉ Labor Day weekend – Memorial Day weekend: Wednesday – Saturday, 10 a.m. – 5 p.m.; Sunday, noon – 5 p.m. Memorial Day weekend - Labor Day weekend: Friday – Saturday, 10 a.m. – 5 p.m.; Sunday, noon – 5 p.m.

The Agua Caliente Cultural Museum evolved out of an Agua Caliente Band of Cahuilla Indians Committee and was established in 1991 as a tribal museum. It is governed by a volunteer board, two-thirds of which must be members of the local Native American tribe. Presently housed in a building owned by the city of Palm Springs, the Agua Caliente is embarking on the construction of a new 98,000-square-foot museum on tribal land. This state-of-the-art facility will espouse the culture and heritage of the Agua Caliente and other Cahuilla bands. The building is scheduled to open in late 2008.

A large portion of the museum's 1,500 Native American objects are owned by the Agua Caliente Band of Cahuilla Indians and are on permanent loan to the museum. Some objects have come from private donors. The collection focuses on Southern California basketry, Cahuilla ceramics, and Palm Springs archeological objects. Agua Caliente is a "story-based" museum. Exhibitions focus on the history and culture of the Cahuilla people and may or may not include items from the collection, about five percent of which is on display (though this will change significantly when the new building opens). Storage is accessible to tribal members and researchers by appointment.

Palm Springs Art Museum

101 Museum Drive
Palm Springs, CA 92262
Phone: 760-325-7186
E-mail: info@psmuseum.org
URL: www.psmuseum.org

☉ October – May: Tuesday, Wednesday, Friday, Saturday, Sunday, 10 a.m. – 5 p.m.; Thursday, noon – 8 p.m. (free from 4 p.m. – 8 p.m.) Closed Monday. June – September: Wednesday, Friday, Saturday, Sunday, 10 a.m. – 5 p.m.; Thursday, noon – 8 p.m.

The Palm Springs Art Museum was founded in 1938 in a one-room facility. Today, the museum is a 125,000-square-foot institution. The current building was designed and built by renowned architect E. Stewart Williams in 1974.

The museum collection includes 1,920 Native American pieces, 170 Mesoamerican objects, and 279 Asian and African artworks and artifacts. Major donors have included George Montgomery (actor, artist, and collector), Kirk and Anne Douglas, and William Holden.

The Native American collection features works by the local Agua Caliente Band of Cahuilla Indians. Other California tribes are represented by excellent examples of works by Pomo, Panamint, Chemehuevi, Washoe, Yokuts, and objects by Southwest tribes including Apache, Hopi, and Navajo. The museum's collections also include prime examples of Navajo textiles and Navajo and Zuni jewelry.

Pacific Grove Museum of Natural History

165 Forest Ave.
Pacific Grove, CA 93950
Phone: 831-648-5716
Fax: 831-372-3256
URL: www.pgmuseum.org

⊙ Tuesday – Saturday, 10 a.m. – 5 p.m.

The Pacific Grove Museum has a variety of ethnic materials that includes objects from Africa, Asia, Australia, Mexico, Central America, Pacific Islands, and South America. It holds more than 2,000 American Indian objects and is particularly rich in northern Native American and Eskimo pieces. The latter were significantly augmented by the collection of Ernst Leffingwell. The research collection is open to qualified researchers by appointment.

Pacific Asia Museum

46 North Los Robles Ave.
Pasadena, CA 91101
Phone: 626-449-2742
URL: www.pacificasiamuseum.org

⊙ Wednesday, Thursday, Saturday, Sunday, 10 a.m. – 5 p.m.; Friday, 10 a.m. – 8 p.m.

The museum's permanent collection contains more than 14,000 rare and representative examples of art and artifacts from Asia and the Pacific Islands, spanning a period of five thousand years.

Chaw'se Regional Museum at Indian Grinding Rock State Historic Park

14881 Pine Grove-Volcano Road
Pine Grove, CA 95665
Phone: 209-296-7488
URL: www.parks.ca.gov/?page_id=553

⊙ Park hours: dawn to dusk. Museum hours: Wednesday – Friday , 11 a.m. – 3 p.m.; Weekends, 10 a.m. – 4 p.m.

Designated as a state park in 1968, this site in the Sierra Nevada foothills has exposed limestone bedrock that is riddled with 1,185 mortar cups and 363 associated petroglyphs created by local Indian groups. A replica Miwok village, including a roundhouse, has been built nearby and the park also features a museum that displays an outstanding collection of Sierra Nevada Indian artifacts. There are approximately 1,500 objects, including over 100 Sierra regional California Indian baskets. Feather regalia, jewelry, arrowpoints, and other tools are on exhibit and additional objects are in visible storage. The collection represents the Northern, Central and Southern Miwok, Maidu, Konkow, Monache, Nisenan, Tubatulabal, Washo, and Foothill Yokuts.

California

Tribal Art Museum Collections *in the* UNITED STATES

Shasta College Museum and Research Center

11555 Old Oregon Trail
Redding, CA 96049
Phone: 530-225-4754
E-mail: dsmith@shastacollege.edu

☺ Monday – Wednesday, 9:30 a.m. – 2:30 p.m.; Thursday, 9:30 a.m. – 2 p.m.

The museum, built in 1972, resembles the adobe of Pierson B. Reading, Shasta County's first permanent white settler. The building is surrounded by an outside display area featuring various aspects of Northern California history.

There are about 500 tribal objects in the collection, mainly baskets and tools that are augmented by a historic photo archive. Most of the material was donated by local residents and Native Americans. They are typically kept in storage unless they are needed for a specific display.

Riverside Municipal Museum

3580 Mission Inn Ave.
Riverside, CA 92501
Phone: 909-826-5273
Fax: 909-369-4970
URL: www.riversideca.gov/museum/

☺ Tuesday – Friday, 9 a.m. – 5 p.m.; Saturday, 10 a.m. – 5 p.m.; Sunday, 11 a.m. – 5 p.m. Closed major holidays.

The Riverside Municipal Museum opened in the basement of City Hall in 1924, after the widow of National Biscuit Company magnate Cornelius Earle Rumsey donated his collection of Native American artifacts to the City of Riverside. Since then, its collections have grown, typically through donations by prominent citizens and organizations. In 1948 it moved to its present location, a post office building that had been constructed in 1914. In the 1960s, under innovative director Charles Hice, the museum broke out of its traditional role as a depository of collectables donated by city notables and moved toward a new existence as a modern museum. New exhibits and community-oriented programs have brought about its current configuration.

The anthropology collection at the Riverside Municipal Museum consists of approximately 20,000 items. About 5,000 of these are Native American baskets, the bulk of which are from the western United States, especially Arizona and California. It also includes seventeenth and eighteenth century Eskimo tools as well as contemporary Inuit steatite sculptures. There is a small collection of Plains beadwork. The museum has an outstanding collection of Native American cradle boards that features examples from every major culture area in North America where the cradle was used. The collection as a whole numbers fifty-eight objects, including twenty-three doll cradles, assembled from over thirty-five tribal groups. The museum also houses a research library related to Northern Native Americans.

Maidu Interpretive Center

1960 Johnson Ranch Drive
Roseville, CA 95661
Phone: 916-774-9534
Fax: 916-772-6161
URL: www.roseville.ca.us/parks/parks_n_facil
ities/facilities/maidu_indian_museum/default.
asp

☉ **Tuesday – Saturday, 9 a.m. – 4 p.m.**

The Maidu Interpretive Center and Historic Site in the central Sierra foothills offer a loop trail that travels through a nature area past ancient petroglyphs and hundreds of bedrock mortars, evidence of Nisenan occupation of the site for thousands of years. The museum displays exhibits portraying the Nisenan, Konkow, and Mountain Maidu way of life.

California State Indian Museum

2618 K Street
Sacramento, CA 95816
Phone: 916-324-0971
URL: www.parks.ca.gov/default.asp?page_id
=486

☉ **Daily, 10 a.m. – 5 p.m.**
Closed Christmas, New Year's, and Thanksgiving.

On the grounds of Sutter's Fort in downtown Sacramento, the California State Indian Museum displays exhibits and artifacts illustrating the culture of the region's earliest inhabitants. The artifacts in the museum include basketry, beadwork, clothing and exhibits about the ongoing traditions of various California Native American groups, including a display about Ishi, the last of the Yahi Indians. Also on display is traditional dance regalia (feather headbands, plume sticks, dance capes and headdresses) as well as musical instruments, such as the foot drum, clapper stick, wood and bone whistles, dance rattles and musical bow. The Central Valley Regional Indian Room focuses on the Indigenous Peoples of the Central Valley, with information about Native American fishing, hunting, tools, trade routes and use of tule, which carpeted the valley's wetlands.

California Museum Resource Center

2505 Port Street
West Sacramento, CA 95691
Phone: 916-375-5901
Fax: 916-375-5913
URL: www.smrc.parks.ca.gov

☉ **Special tours limited to ten people or fewer may be arranged by telephone.**

For more than a century, the state of California has received generous donations of artworks from individual citizens. As stewards of these cultural resources, the CMRC staff researches, documents, preserves, exhibits, and provides access to these collections. For Native art, the collection's primary focus is North American Indian material culture. Artifacts include examples of basketry, pottery, beadwork and textiles.

California Department of Parks and Recreation State Archaeological Collections Research Facility

2505 Port St.
West Sacramento, CA 95691
Phone: 916-375-5921
Fax: 916-375-5913
E-mail: gfarr@parks.ca.gov

☉ **Daily (by appointment), 8:30 a.m. – 5 p.m. Closed on state holidays.**

The State Archaeological Collections Research Facility is a unique resource in California. In addition to providing a location to process and research recent excavations in California State Parks, the facility is home to an extensive collection of artifacts and archaeological records.

The SACRF houses an array of collections that have been recovered by state archaeologists and researchers. Artifacts from California State Parks in Monterey, Fort Ross, Old Sacramento, Old Town San Diego, San Juan Bautista and many more are housed in the facility. Many of the objects are cross-referenced into artifact type collections, which are groups of objects similar in structure and use that have been assembled for use by researchers. The type collections offered at the SACRF include a bottle type collection, a ceramic type collection, a makers' mark collection, and a vertebrate faunal collection.

The oldest excavated site in the California State Park system that is represented in the SACRF is Duncan's Landing Rockshelter on the Sonoma Coast State Beach (CA-SON-348/H). Its lowest levels date to 8500 BP. This three-meter-deep shell midden site produced obsidian projectile points, bone tools (awls and fish gorges), shell ornaments, beads (olivella, land snail, and soapstone), and milling equipment. Recent studies have been undertaken by researchers at UC Davis to develop data on past climate events using oxygen isotope testing on mussel shells with reliable radiocarbon dates that have been obtained from this site.

Numerous archaeological excavations at the coastal location of Fort Ross, which over time has been occupied by the Kashaya Indians, the Russian-America Company, and families of ranchers and loggers, have produced artifacts reflecting the many cultures that inhabited this part of the rugged upper Sonoma Coast.

Excavations under and around the last standing structure of the Santa Cruz Mission and from the mission at San Juan Bautista have also yielded many items of everyday life. Excavations on neophyte Indian family housing sites have unearthed a variety of illuminating artifacts, some dating from the 1820s.

The John Marsh Mansion, constructed by one of the earliest white settlers of the Central Valley, was built on top of an Indian midden. Excavations at that site have revealed several layers of culture of the peoples occupying the lower San Joaquin Delta area, including a layer of the enigmatic "Meganos" culture.

There is little that most would refer to as "art" at the SACRF, but as a repository for artifacts, it is unparalled in the state.

Mingei International Museum

1439 El Prado, Balboa Park
San Diego, CA 92101
North County Satellite:
155 West Grand Avenue
Escondido, CA 92025
Phone: 619-239-0003
Fax: 619-239-0605
E-mail: mingei@mingei.org
URL: www.mingei.org

☉ **Tuesday – Sunday, 10 a.m. – 4 p.m.**
North Country Satellite: Tuesday –
Saturday, 1 p.m. – 4 p.m.
Closed Mondays and national holidays.

Mingei is a special word increasingly used throughout the world to designate "arts of the people." It was coined by the revered scholar, Dr. Soetsu Yanagi, who combined the Japanese words for all people *(min)* and art *(gei)*. Joined by potters Shoji Hamada and Kaniro Kawai, Yanagi formed the Mingei Association of Japan, which was responsible for the foundation of the first international crafts museum in Tokyo. Martha Longenecker, a professor at San Diego State University, encountered the members of the Mingei Association and, inspired by their vision, in 1978 established Mingei International as a place where the finest examples of arts from all cultures of the world could speak for themselves. The museum was first located in a small space in a shopping center. Over the years it grew dramatically, and in 1996 it moved to its present space in Balboa Park. In 2003, it opened a satellite space in Escondido.

The museum has a rapidly expanding collection of art objects from one hundred countries. It emphasizes Asian artworks but features approximately 15,000 tribal objects. Among these is an important collection of embroidery and silver jewelry from the many non-Han cultures of Guizhou, China. Ethiopian and Yoruba objects, an Indonesian collection rich in Dayak objects, and a collection of artworks from Ladakh, India, are also prominent in the museum's holdings. Navaho and Tibetan pieces are also included.

The museum's pre-Columbian collection represents a variety of cultures from Mexico. It also spans Central and South America. A gift in 2000 from an anonymous foundation made possible the acquisition of the Greaves Collection of pre-Columbian Marine Animals. This unique assemblage of more than 250 objects in ceramic, stone, metal, and textile focuses on representations of marine fauna and marine-associated mythological themes as found in the pre-Columbian art of the Americas.

Approximately five percent of the collection is on display at any one time, but the exhibitions are constantly changing, so a great deal of the collection cycles through the installations over time. In its first twenty-five years, the museum organized and presented 109 major exhibitions, some of which have continued to reach a nationwide audience as they travel to other museums.

California

San Diego Museum of Man

1350 El Prado, Balboa Park
San Diego, CA 92101
Phone: 619-239-2001
Fax: 619-239-2749
URL: www.museumofman.org

☺ Daily, 10 a.m. – 4:30 p.m.
Closed Thanksgiving, Christmas, and
New Year's Day.

The Panama-California Exposition opened on January 1, 1915, and within it an anthropology exhibit titled *The Story of Man through the Ages* enjoyed considerable public acclaim. It had been assembled by Ales Hrdlicka of the Smithsonian and was the fruit of expeditions to Alaska, Siberia, Africa, and the Philippines, as well as loans from European institutions. As the exposition neared its close in November 1915, a farsighted group of San Diegans formed the San Diego Museum Association. Led by prominent citizen George Marston, they retained the valuable collections and established a museum of anthropology. Edgar L. Hewett became the first director, and important collections followed, notably the Jessop Weapon Collection and the Scripps Egyptian Collection. Fieldwork by museum staff in the 1930s focused on prehistoric sites of Southern California. Through the efforts of pioneer archaeologist Malcolm J. Rogers, hundreds of sites, many now destroyed by development, were recorded.

Because of the museum's concentration on anthropology, its name was changed in 1942 to the Museum of Man. In 1966, the collection and research focus of the museum was narrowed to the peoples of the Western Americas. Important collections continued to be acquired, among them the Gildred Collection of pre-Hispanic Peruvian ceramics, and the Cannon Collection of Southern Californian Indian basketry. The museum's collection is now in excess of 72,000 items plus 37,000 historic photographs (mostly of Native Americans) as well as unquantified archaeological holdings.

Permanent exhibits explore the Maya, ancient Egypt, the Kumeyaay Indians of San Diego County, human evolution, and the human life cycle.

Adan E. Treganza Anthropology Museum

3rd floor of Science
San Francisco State University
1600 Holloway Ave.
San Francisco, CA 94132
Phone: 415-338-1642
E-mail: yamamoto@sfsu.edu

☺ Monday – Friday, 10 a.m. – 3 p.m.
(when there is an exhibition).

Founded in 1968, the Treganza holds a number of Native American ethnological artifacts as well as objects from Oceania and Asia. Most of the material has been field collected by faculty members.

Of note among the museum's 2,500 objects are incised gourds from northeastern Nigeria, African musical instruments collected by David Gamble, the Meadows mask collection, California and Indonesian baskets, and a collection of Papua New Guinea tourist art carvings. The collection is occassionally drawn upon for special exhibitions. In storage, the objects are accessible by appointment to those doing research on material culture.

Asian Art Museum of San Francisco

200 Larkin Street
San Francisco, CA 94102
Phone: 415-581-3500
E-mail: pr@asianart.org (public relations)
URL: www.asianart.org

☉ **Tuesday – Sunday, 10 a.m. – 5 p.m.; with extended evening hours every Thursday until 9 p.m. Closed Mondays, New Year's Day, Thanksgiving, Christmas, and during certain large-scale Civic Center events (call for details).**

The Asian Art Museum holds one of the most comprehensive collections of Asian art in the world. Spanning 6,000 years, its scope and breadth enable the museum to provide an introduction to all the major traditions of Asian art and culture. Well known in the scholarly world, the collection contains rare and exceptional objects that are often referenced in journals and textbooks. It began as the vast private collection of Chicago millionaire Avery Brundage, who in 1959 agreed to donate part of it to the city of San Francisco on the condition a new museum be built to house it. In 1966, the new facility opened in a space constructed as a wing of the M.H. de Young Memorial Museum in Golden Gate Park. Brundage continued to collect for the next decade and in 1969 he forged an agreement with the city to provide for an independent Committee of Asian Art and Culture to run the museum as a seperate entity from the de Young. In 1973 the institution—until then known officially as the Center for Asian Art and Culture—was renamed the Asian Art Museum of San Francisco. Upon his death in 1975, Brundage bequeathed his remaining Asian art to the museum, bringing his donation to more than 7,700 Asian art objects.

The city's collection of Asian art was merged with the Brundage Collection and acquisitions have been ongoing. Today the collection includes nearly 15,000 objects ranging from tiny jades to monumental sculptures of stone, bronze, and wood. The collection also includes paintings on screens, hanging scrolls, porcelains and ceramics, lacquers, textiles, furniture, arms and armor, puppets, and basketry. While the collection is relatively small for a major museum, the quality is remarkable. It is the largest museum in the United States devoted exclusively to the arts of Asia.

In addition to the high arts of China, Japan, and Korea, the cultures of Indonesia, Burma, Vietnam, and the Philippines are represented through sculpture, textiles, jewelry, ceramics, terra-cotta works, and paintings. Particular highlights are a sizeable collection of stone and bronze material from Angkor Wat, a comprehensive collection of Thai ceramics, and a collection of krises (daggers) from Indonesia, Malaysia, and the Philippines.

In 2003 the museum moved out of the cramped Brundage wing of the de Young and into a new home in the former Main Library building in the Civic Center, which had been retrofitted and expanded by noted architect Gae Aulenti. The new building allows for special exhibitions and a broader presentation of this important collection.

California

California Academy of Sciences

875 Howard Street
San Francisco, CA 94103-3009
Phone: 415-321-8000
URL: www.calacademy.org

☉ **The Academy in Golden Gate Park is closed until late 2008 when rebuilding is complete.**

Founded in 1853 to survey and study the vast resources of California and beyond, the California Academy of Sciences is the oldest scientific institution in the West. In its early days, spurred by their concern over the natural environment during the California Gold Rush, the Academy consisted of a group of naturalists who met weekly and presented scientific papers on topics of interest to a growing membership of San Francisco citizens. As the collection of specimens from the field grew in number and scope, the important scientific work of identifying, classifying and naming species, known as "systematics," began. The museum moved into a six-story building in 1891 and for fifteen years its natural history specimens remained a popular and growing attraction. The building and virtually all of its holdings were destroyed in the 1906 earthquake, but even as the city burned, a two-year Academy expedition to the Galapagos Islands was gathering the material that would form the nucleus of the institution's new collections. The Academy was rebuilt in Golden Gate Park, opposite the de Young Museum, in vastly expanded quarters. Today it ranks among the world's ten largest natural history museums. The Golden Gate Park complex, which had grown with piecemeal additions over the decades, was recently demolished. A new, integrated building designed by Renzo Piano is scheduled to open in 2008. The Academy is presently operating in temporary administrative offices.

The Academy's anthropology collection contains approximately 16,000 objects representing material cultures from peoples throughout the world. The department actively collects material of the indigenous cultures of western North America (exclusive of Mexico) and of the Pacific Rim, including all Pacific islands and East Asia. Current strengths of the collection are holdings from the U.S. Southwest and the Pacific Islands, and basketry from California. Earlier years of collecting have yielded both ethnographic and archaeological materials from East Africa, the Middle East, Europe, and Central and South America

Highlights of the collection include the Elgueta Collection, consisting of over 1,000 ancient Mayan objects from Chalchitan and Pichikil collected before 1906; the Elkus Collection of Native American art with more than 1,700 Native American objects, including textiles, jewelry, baskets, pottery, works of art on paper, kachina carvings, and beadwork; the Rollo Beck Collection of more than 400 objects from at least fourteen distinct Pacific Island groups, including the Solomon, Fiji, and Santa Cruz Islands; and the Liebes Collection of approximately 1,000 Native Alaskan objects, primarily bone and ivory tools, and ivory craft items.

de Young Museum

50 Hagiwara Tea Garden Drive
San Francisco, CA 94118
Phone: 415-750-3600
URL: www.thinker.org

⊙ **Tuesday - Sunday, 9:30 a.m. – 5 p.m.;
with extended hours until 8:45 p.m.
every Friday.**

The de Young is one of two museums functioning under the administration of the Fine Arts Museums of San Francisco. It is the central museum of the city of San Francisco. Founded in 1895 in Golden Gate Park on the site of the 1894 California Midwinter International Exposition as the Memorial Museum, it was later renamed in honor of newspaper publisher M. H. de Young, who was instrumental in its founding and development. The museum was badly damaged in the 1989 Loma Prieta earthquake and was subsequently demolished. A new, state-of-the-art building designed by the noted Swiss architectural firm Herzog & de Meuron opened on the same site in October of 2005 with tribal and ancient art as a major focus.

The incomparable Marcia and John Friede Collection of New Guinea art is the centerpiece of the new museum. More than 400 spectacular objects from this vast island are beautifully installed. Works include a monumental male figure from the Biwat culture that has been radiocarbon dated to the early eleventh century; a towering Sepik hook formerly in the collection of Surrealist artist Roberto Matta; a rare Torres Strait mortuary mask made of turtle shell and cassowary feathers; and a dramatic middle Sepik dance costume with attached clan masks. The Oceanic gallery also features spectacular woodcarvings from Polynesia and Micronesia, including a monumental figure from Nukuoro. Indonesia's Outer Islands are highlighted with masterpieces from the Kuhn Collection.

A large gallery dedicated to African art represents more than eighty cultural and ethnic groups and celebrates the striking cultural richness and diversity of this remarkable art form. Highlights include one of the oldest known Dogon wood sculptures in existence (AD 1200), a nail figure from the Kongo collected at the turn of the twentieth century by the ethnographer R. Visser, a menacing seven-headed bush spirit from the Ijo people of Nigeria, and a splendid metallic textile reminiscent of traditional Kente cloth by contemporary artist El Anatsui.

The Native American galleries contain extraordinary examples of the arts of the Americas (Maya, Teotihuacan, Gulf Coast and Central Mexico, Central America, Andean) which were intended for the glorification of gods or kings. Works from Mesoamerican and Andean cultures date from 2000 BC through mid-sixteenth century AD and include the largest and most important group of Teotihuacan wall murals outside of Mexico, which were bequeathed to the museum by Harald Wagner. A remarkable Late Classic Maya Stela of a regalia-laden queen dating to AD 761 is prominently displayed at the entrance to the gallery. Its acquisition was made possible by the late Phyllis Wattis, who was a major donor for all parts of the AOA collection. A monumental Olmec stone head presides over a gallery displaying exquisite West Mexico ceramics from the Lewis K. Land Collection. Elegant Maya ceramics from the Gail and Alec Merriam Collection are also featured in a special gallery.

California

El Museo Mexicano/ The Mexican Museum

Fort Mason Center
Building D
San Francisco, CA 94123
Phone: 415-202-9700
Fax: 415-441-7683
E-mail: info@mexicanmuseum.org
URL: www.mexicanmuseum.org

☉ **Peter Rodriguez Gallery Hours:**
Wednesday - Saturday, 11 a.m. – 5 p.m.

The Mexican Museum, initially located in the heart of San Francisco's Mission District, was founded in 1975 by San Francisco resident and artist Peter Rodríguez. The museum was the realization of his vision that an institution be created in the United States to exhibit the aesthetic expression of the Mexican and Mexican-American people.

Presently located in Fort Mason near the Golden Gate Bridge, the Mexican Museum is poised at the brink of one of the most exciting phases in its twenty-six-year history. It is constructing a new building in the downtown Yerba Buena Arts Center. When it is completed, it will provide space in which to expand the museum's education and public programs. This new facility will house a unique collection of over 12,000 objects representing thousands of years of Mexican history and culture within the Americas.

The museum's permanent collection includes pre-Conquest and colonial period artifacts as well as modern and contemporary Mexican, Latino, and Chicano art. The pre-Conquest collection spans thousands of years prior to the sixteenth century. It features examples of ceramic figures, beads and bowls from Mexican regions and cultures such as Chupícuaro, Colima, Huastec, Jalisco, Nayarit, Remojadas, Toltec, Maya, Zapotec, Aztec, Veracruz, and Yucatán. It also includes dramatic vessels, tools and mythological figures from the Inca, Nazca, Moche and Chancay civilizations of Peru.

Museum of the African Diaspora

685 Mission Street (at Third)
San Francisco, CA 94105
phone: 415-358-7200
fax: 415-358-7252
URL: www.moadsf.org

☉ **Monday, Wednesday, Friday,**
Saturday, 10 a.m. – 6 p.m.; Sunday, noon
– 5 p.m. Open until 9 p.m. on
Thursdays.

A new international museum, based in San Francisco, MoAD initiates collaborative ventures with institutions of similar vision from around the world to present the best aspects of art and culture to emerge from the African diaspora. More than an art museum, MoAD is a collection of stories and a repository of information to be shared with all who wish to know about the African diaspora.

Embracing the newest applications in media technology, MoAD features an interactive theater and immersive exhibitions. While the emphasis is on the diaspora experience outside of Africa, exhibitions of African tribal art are planned and are considered to be an important part of the institution's mission.

Museum of Craft and Folk Art

51 Yerba Buena Lane
San Francisco, CA 94103
Phone: 415-227-4888
Fax: 415-227-4351
E-mail: info@mocfa.org
URL: www.mocfa.org

⊙ **Tuesday – Friday, 11 a.m. – 6 p.m.;**
Saturday and Sunday, 10 a.m. – 5 p.m.
Closed Monday and on major holidays.

The Museum of Craft & Folk Art is the only museum of its kind in Northern California. Founded in San Francisco in 1983, the museum moved from Fort Mason downtown to the Yerba Buena Center in November 2005. The museum is a non-collecting institution and is focused on mounting temporary exhibitions. The museum's craft exhibitions emphasize the work of skilled artists giving new life to glass, clay, fiber, wood, and metal as vessels, clothing, furniture, and jewelry. In addition to contemporary craft, the museum also addresses American folk art and traditional cultural art from around the world. Accompanying its exhibitions are educational programs and publications dedicated to the understanding of human expression, ranging from utilitarian objects to contemporary art.

Bowers Museum

2002 North Main Street
Santa Ana, CA 92706
Phone: 714-567-3600
URL: www.bowers.org

⊙ **Tuesday – Sunday, 10 a.m. – 4 p.m.**
Closed on Mondays, 4th of July,
Thanksgiving Day, Christmas Day, and
New Year's Day.

The Charles W. Bowers Memorial Museum first opened its doors in 1936 as a city-run museum devoted primarily to the history of Orange County. In October of 1992, a renovated and much larger Bowers Museum opened its doors. Since this highly successful reopening, the museum has presented more than thirty special exhibitions focusing on art and culture around the world, opened six permanent galleries, and has been accredited by the American Association of Museums. The permanent installations include galleries for Native California art, the art of shamanism in the pre-Columbian Americas, and the history of Orange County. Recent temporary exhibitions have addressed the art of the Himalayas and Ancient Egypt.

The museum holds approximately 32,000 African, Oceanic, pre-Columbian, and Native American objects, most received through donation. Only a small percentage are on display. The objects in storage are mainly used for traveling exhibitions but can be accessed by qualified researchers by appointment.

California

Santa Barbara Museum of Natural History

2559 Puesta del Sol Road
Santa Barbara, CA 93105
Phone: 805-682-4711
Fax: 805-569-3170
URL: www.sbnature.org

☉ Daily, 10 a.m. – 5 p.m.
Closed New Year's Day, first Friday in August (Fiesta), Thanksgiving, Christmas Eve (3 p.m.), and Christmas.

The Santa Barbara Museum of Natural History was founded 1916 and opened at its present location near the Santa Barbara Mission in 1923. Several exhibit wings were added to the Spanish Colonial Revival–style building in the 1920s and '30s. A state-of-the-art Collections and Research Center, housing departments of Anthropology, Vertebrate and Invertebrate Zoology, and Earth Sciences, opened in 1991.

Materials from indigenous cultures are housed in the Anthropology Department. More than 5,000 ethnographic artifacts represent over 500 Native cultures with primary emphasis on western North America, which encompasses California, the Southwest, the Northwest Coast, the Western Arctic, and the Great Plains. Africa, Oceania, and Mesoamerica are represented by small numbers of objects. Nearly all the ethnographic artifacts in the museum's collection have been donated by individuals including early collectors such as philanthropist Max Fleischmann, noted artist Fernand Lungren, and Mr. & Mrs. Philip B. Stewart. The Plains Indian collection features a Cheyenne painted buckskin coat, c. 1870, which is decorated with pictographic scenes depicting Cheyennes raiding a Crow camp to obtain horses. Another pictographic panel, painted on muslin c. 1890 by a Hunkpapa Sioux artist, portrays scenes from a historic 1869 battle called "Killed 30 Crows." Other highlights of the museum's collection include more than 1,000 baskets made by Native peoples throughout western North America; many Northwest Coast wood carvings; textiles of the Southwest, Mexico and Central America; and featherwork of South American tropical forest peoples.

Archaeological collections include approximately 75,000 specimens from 200 sites around the Santa Barbara area and the Northern Channel Islands of California, representing all major periods of prehistory.

Most of the museum's exhibition space is dedicated to permanent exhibits focused on the natural history of the Santa Barbara region. One gallery, the Chumash Indian Hall, is permanently dedicated to exhibiting the material culture of this local Indian group, for which the museum houses one of the world's largest collections of artifacts. It includes the world's foremost collection of rare Chumash basketry and fiberwork, consisting of forty-five ethnographic pieces and some 100 archaeological specimens. A fine basket by Juana Basilia, c. 1815, features designs from Spanish colonial coins and words of dedication woven at over 200 stitches per square inch. Museum anthropologists work closely with the Chumash community to present and interpret the material.

Collections not on display are housed in the Collections and Research Center, where they are accessible by appointment with curators. The museum's 40,000-volume reference library is another valuable resource for researchers.

Tribal Art **Museum Collections** *in the* **UNITED STATES**

de Saisset Museum

500 El Camino Real
Santa Clara, CA 95053-0550
Phone: 408-554-4528
E-mail: rnadel@scu.edu
URL: www.scu.edu/desaisset

☉ **Tuesday – Sunday, 11 a.m. – 4 p.m. during regularly scheduled exhibitions.**

The de Saisset Museum at Santa Clara University is a free museum of art and history serving the region immediately south of San Francisco. The museum was founded through a bequest from Isabel de Saisset in 1955. Since then its collections have expanded to include thousands of objects, including approximately fifty Native American projectile points and charm stones, 113 Native American baskets, and twenty-three works of ethnographic African art.

The de Saisset's permanent installation includes a gallery dedicated to California History, which includes much of its Native American material. Objects in storage are available to qualified researchers by appointment.

Triton Museum of Art

1505 Warburton Ave.
Santa Clara, CA 95050
Phone: 408-247-3754
Fax: 408-247-3796
E-mail: info@tritonmuseum.org
URL: www.tritonmuseum.org

☉ **Daily, 11 a.m. – 5 p.m.; Thursdays, 11 a.m. – 9 p.m.**

The Triton Museum of Art was founded by rancher, lawyer and art patron W. Robert Morgan in 1965. Two years later it moved to its present location in Santa Clara. The current building opened in 1987.

The museum hosts changing exhibitions of contemporary art. Its only permanent gallery is dedicated to the Native American art collection of Austen D. Warburton, a Santa Clara attorney and active community member who passed away in 1995 and bequeathed his entire 2,268-object collection to the museum. The installation features 170 objects, including some fine examples of Anasazi pottery.

Shasta State Historic Park

15312 Highway 299
Shasta, CA 96087
Phone: 530-243-8194
E-mail: shastashp@snowcrest.net

☉ **Wednesday – Sunday, 10 a.m. – 5 p.m.**

The Courthouse Museum and Shasta State Historic park opened in 1950 and was expanded in 2000. Its collection includes historic Native American baskets, mostly from the turn of the twentieth century. The collection is largely the result of private donors who have gifted their collections to the State of California.

California

Cantor Arts Center at Stanford University

Lomita Drive and Museum Way
Stanford, CA 94305-5060
Phone: 650-723-4177
Fax: 650-725-0464
URL: www.stanford.edu/dept/ccva

☉ **Wednesday – Sunday, 11 a.m. –
5 p.m.; Thursday, 11 a.m. – 8 p.m.
Closed on Mondays and Tuesdays,
Thanksgiving, Christmas, and New
Year's Day.**

The Cantor Arts Center began as the Leland Stanford Jr. Museum and was conceived in tandem with the founding of Stanford University in 1891. The Stanford family, including Leland Jr., the founders' son whose name the university commemorates, traveled the world collecting objects of art and cultural interest. The museum, which opened in 1894, was originally created to make this collection available to students and the public. It has withstood natural disasters and periodic neglect, only to be resurrected, renewed, and expanded with its collections stronger than ever.

A dozen years after it opened, the 1906 San Francisco earthquake destroyed two-thirds of the building and much of the collection. In 1945 the repaired facility was closed due to neglect. In 1963 efforts began to refurbish the museum, a slow process that was terminated by the 1989 Loma Prieta earthquake, which severely damaged the building and again forced it to close. This time recovery was faster and the museum reopened in 1999, significantly expanded and revitalized, as the Iris & B. Gerald Cantor Center for Visual Arts

The center's African art collection consists of approximately 500 works, with a comprehensive selection of figurative art from sub-Saharan Africa. Pieces in the collection have been selected for their aesthetic merit and cultural significance. Approximately seventy objects are currently on display in the gallery.

The Oceania and Indonesia collections feature 300 art objects and an additional 150 textiles. Fine objects from both collections share space in one gallery, in which Batak material is well represented.

The Native American collection focuses on North America, especially California, the Southwest, and the Northwest Coast. Of particular interest are baskets and related objects from the daily life of the Yurok, Karuk, and Hupa tribes of Northern California collected by John Daggett soon after the 1849 Gold Rush. This group of objects was part of the museum's original collection and has since been both supplemented and broadened. Many of the other Native American objects came from the collection of Jane Stanford in the late nineteenth century.

The Ancient Americas collection of about 200 works of art, includes terracotta figures and vessels from West Mexico and a representative selection of works from other cultures in Mesoamerica, notably the Maya, Zapotec, and Veracruz. Central American and Peruvian cultures are also represented. Fine representative examples of ancient ceramics from the southwestern United States and northern Mexico, including Mimbres, Anasazi, and Casas Grandes, are included in the Ancient Americas display.

Victor and Paula Zurcher, the Christensen Fund, Marc and Ruth Franklin, Dr. and Mrs. Ralph Spiegl, and Mrs. Frederick Henry Colburn are among major donors of these collections.

Gatekeeper's Museum & Marion Steinbach Indian Basket Museum

130 West Lake Boulevard
Tahoe City, CA 96145
Phone: 530-583-1762
Fax: 530-583-8992
E-mail: info@northtahoemuseums.org

☉ May 1 – June 15 and September 1 – 30: Wednesday – Sunday, 11 a.m. – 5 p.m. June 16 – August 30: daily, 11 a.m. – 5 p.m. October: Weekends, 11 a.m. – 3 p.m. November – April: Open by appointment, weather and schedules permitting.

Operated by the North Lake Tahoe Historical Society, the Gatekeeper's Museum is a reconstruction of the original cabin used by the "gatekeeper," who monitored the flow of water out of Lake Tahoe into the Truckee River. The original cabin was destroyed by arson fire but was rebuilt as a museum in 1981. The museum houses historical exhibits that focus on the local Native inhabitants and the development of the Tahoe Basin.

The Marion Steinbach Indian Basket Museum was built onto the Gatekeeper's Museum in 1994. This museum houses Steinbach's personal collection of over 800 baskets, pottery and artifacts, representing eighty-five tribes, all west of the Mississippi. Every item in the extensive basket collection is on display. The other exhibits in the Gatekeeper's Museum are rotated regularly and approximately seventy percent of the total collection is on display at any given time.

Patrick's Point State Park, Sumêg Village

4150 Patrick's Point Drive
Trinidad, CA 95570
Phone: 707-677-3570
URL: www.parks.ca.gov/default.asp?page_id=417

☉ Daily, 8 a.m. to sunset.

The idea to build a reconstructed Yurok village at Patrick's Point State Park was first talked about in the late 1920s. The actual construction work started in 1989 and was completed in 1990. The resulting Sumêg Village consists of two canoes, three living houses, two sweat houses, a dance pit, one cleansing pool, and three dress houses.

The intent of the village was to educate people of all walks of life about the Yurok culture as well as to be a place for cultural ceremonies and gatherings. All areas of the village are open to the general public with the exception of one sweat house, which is available only for Native American cultural use. The Yurok, Karuk and the Hoopa tribes gather on the site on the third week of June for a traditional Brush Dance.

In 1997, a Native American Plant Garden was established featuring plants that were used by the local Yuroks. The plantings in the garden are representative of the plants used for medicinal, basketry, subsistence, and ceremonial purposes.

California

Grace Hudson Museum and Sun House

431 S. Main
Ukiah, CA 95482
Phone: 707-467-2836
Fax: 707-467-2835
E-mail: gracehudson@pacific.net
URL: www.gracehudsonmuseum.org

☉ Wednesday – Saturday, 10 a.m. –
4:30 p.m.; Sunday, noon – 4:30 p.m.
Closed holidays.

Since its inauguration in 1986, the Grace Hudson Museum has become an increasingly important cultural and educational resource for Northern California. The museum is an art, history and anthropology institution focusing on the lifeworks of artist
Grace Carpenter Hudson (1865–1937) and her ethnologist husband, Dr. John W.
Hudson (1857–1936). The museum's collections consist of more than 30,000
interrelated objects, with significant holdings of Pomo Indian artifacts (particularly
basketry), ethnographic field notes, unpublished manuscripts, historic photographs,
and a comprehensive collection of Hudson's paintings. The museum is located in the
four-acre Hudson-Carpenter Park, which features a basketry garden containing
plants used by Pomo Indian weavers to create their baskets.

Changing interdisciplinary exhibitions and public programs at the museum emphasize western American art, California Indian cultures, the history of California's
diverse North Coast region, and the work of contemporary regional artists.

Held-Poage Memorial Home and Research Library

603 West Perkins Street
Ukiah, CA 95482
Phone: 707-462-6969
E-mail: mchs@pacific.net

☉ Monday – Friday, 1 p.m. – 4 p.m.

The Held-Poage Memorial Home and Research Library is a window into Mendocino
County's past. The library contains more than 4,500 books covering local, state
and national history, as well as over 13,500 Northern California historical documents and artifacts, including Mendocino County Native basketry.

William P. Held, known as "Billy," served in the California State Legislature
between 1904–1912. He was elected Mayor of Ukiah in 1928 and in 1932 he
became judge of the local Superior Court, where he served for twelve years.

The Held-Poage Memorial Home and Research Library Trust Fund was established in 1976 to preserve archival materials relating to county and state history.
The trust's holdings were greatly augmented in 1983 when Estle Beard, lifetime
Mendocino County resident and historian, left his extensive collection to the society's growing holdings.

Channel Islands National Park

1901 Spinnaker Drive
Ventura, CA 93001
Phone: 805-658-5725
Fax: 805-658-5799

☺ The park is open all year. The Robert
J. Lagomarsino Visitor Center in Ventura
is open daily from 8:30 a.m. – 5 p.m.

Comprised of five in a chain of eight Southern California islands near Los Angeles, Channel Islands National Park is home to a wide variety of nationally and internationally significant natural and cultural resources. The islands were occupied by the Chumash and Gabrielino peoples for a period of more than 6,000 years, but they were removed to mission settlements in the nineteenth century. The islands contain hundreds of identified Indian settlement sites, though none are particularly well marked or interpreted. The Santa Barbara Museum of Natural History is the primary repository for the park's archeological and ethnographic items.

Whiskeytown National Recreation Area

14412 Kennedy Memorial Drive
Whiskeytown, CA 96095
Phone: 530-242-3400
Fax: 530-246-5154
E-mail: clinton_k_kane@nps.gov
URL: www.nps.gov/whis

☺ Visitor Center: Open daily
Labor Day – Memorial Day weekend,
10 a.m. – 4 p.m.
Memorial Day Weekend – Labor Day,
9 a.m. – 6 p.m.

The Whiskeytown National Recreation Area, near the California/Oregon border, was established in 1975. It includes a Wintu Indian archaeological site and an accompanying museum display. A storage facility was built off-site in the 1980s. The museum's collection includes Native American Wintu objects obtained through field collection over the last thirty years, primarily obsidian pieces, projectile points, and various tools that date prehistory to over 5,000 years old. Though the public facility has very few objects on display, the total collection of Wintu artifacts is in excess of 90,000 objects. Storage is accessible mainly by scholarly or research requests.

Tribal Art Museum Collections in the UNITED STATES

The Nomad Museum of Body Adornment and Tribal Arts

616 NW Arizona
Bend, OR 97701
Phone: 541-617-8845
E-mail: blake@nomadmuseum.com
URL: www.nomadmuseum.com

☉ **Tuesday – Saturday, 11 a.m. – 7 p.m.**

The Nomad Museum opened in Bend, Oregon, in 1998. It plans to move to a permanent location in the summer of 2007. Its collection examines body adornment and includes earrings, ear plugs, septum ornaments, and labrets. In addition, there are necklaces, masks, skirts, penis gourds, and related objects of personal ornament. The core of the museum's artifacts was collected by the director's grandmother, Dr. Naomi M. Coval, and his mentor, Father Daniel Jensen, during the 1930s through the 1960s. Both traveled extensively throughout the world and visited or lived among countless indigenous peoples.

The museum showcases jewelry and related personal finery from dozens of the world's notable adorned cultures. It features an extensive collection of pre-Columbian jewelry fabricated in gold, silver, copper, wood, jade, and obsidian, as well as four archaic Chinese jade ear plugs dating from 3000 BC. Nearly all of the museum's 500 items of adornment are on display, but unconserved media, including hundreds of reels of super 8 and 16 mm footage documenting now-extinct cultures filmed by Dr. Coval in the '50s and '60s is in storage waiting for resources that will allow them to be archived and preserved.

Columbia Gorge Discovery Center and Museum

5000 Discovery Drive
The Dalles, OR 97058
Phone: 541-296-8600
Fax: 541-298-8660
E-mail: Info@gorgediscovery.org
URL: www.gorgediscovery.org

☉ **Daily, 9 a.m. – 5 p.m.
Closed Thanksgiving, Christmas, and New Year's Day.**

The facility opened in 1997 as the federally designated official interpretive center for the Columbia River Gorge National Scenic Area. The extensive space features a collection of 7,000 ethnographic objects, of which 990 are on loan from the Winquatt Collection. About two-thirds of the pieces are points and arrowheads.

Most noteworthy is the basket collection from the Pacific Northwest and comparative pieces from throughout the country. Other objects of note are pestles, mortars, paint pots, purses, and necklaces. Only a small percentage of the collection is on display, but storage is accessible for research.

University of Oregon Museum of Natural and Cultural History

1680 E. 15th Ave.
Eugene, OR 97403-1224
Phone: 541-346-3024
Fax: 541-346-5334
E-mail: mnh@uoregon.edu
URL: natural-history.uoregon.edu

⊙ **Tuesday – Sunday, 11 a.m. – 5 p.m.**

The University of Oregon Museum was founded in 1932 and the current building opened in 1987. Following the creation of the museum, it began to receive gifts of Oregon and Northwest ethnographic materials. Faculty members in anthropology and in geography have added similar material, and the museum now holds the largest and most important collection of archaeological materials from Oregon, a group of objects that spans 15,000 years. The museum also holds one of Oregon's most significant collections of Native American cultural artifacts. Another part of the collection features textiles, musical instruments, weapons, and other objects representing traditional technologies and everyday life from Southeast Asia, the Philippines, Africa, Oceania (in particular, New Guinea) and Africa (including Ethiopia, Mozambique, and Congo). Together, these collections comprise more than half a million objects.

Among the museum's holdings are items discovered by Dr. Thomas Condon, the founding father of Oregon geology, during his nineteenth and twentieth century explorations of the John Day region. Material discovered by pioneering archaeologist Dr. Luther Cressman during his early twentieth century desert cave excavations is also included. Important artifacts include an important cache of 10,000-year-old sagebrush bark sandals, extensive fossil collections, and several hundred western Indian baskets made before 1900.

Displayable ethnographic items from outside the United States include more than 900 from Africa, 700 from Asia, 600 from Oceania, 550 from Central America, and about 200 each from the Philippines and South America. The ethnographic textile catalog contains more than 200 total entries, with a series of complete costumes from eastern Europe and Southeast Asia forming important components. Collections worthy of display in terms of significance and condition (as opposed to collections purely of research value) are estimated to total about 30,000 items, although fewer than five percent of them are on display at any one time.

The museum's collections division is also the state repository of Oregon's geological, biological, and cultural specimens. These include definitive Mesozoic fossils, the world's oldest shoes, an unparalleled collection of ancient and modern basketry, and evidence of North America's oldest known house.

Favell Museum

125 West Main Street
Klamath Falls, OR 97601
Phone: 541-882-9996
Fax: 541-850-0125
E-mail: favellmuseum@earthlink.net
URL: www.favellmuseum.org

☺ Monday – Saturday, 9:30 a.m. –
5:30 p.m.

The Favell Museum was founded in 1972 and its collections deal primarily with Native American objects from the western United States. Hundreds of obsidian arrowheads, Columbia River exhibits, and pottery make up the bulk of the collection. Most of the collection was purchased by founders Gene and Winifred Favell, though a small number of individual artifacts were donated. Several collections come from archeological sites such as Nicolarsen Cave, Cougar Mountain Cave, and Humboldt Bay, California. The display includes some examples of Anasazi pottery, Plains beadwork, and a sizable collection of Native American basketry. There are also three exhibits of South American objects.

Nearly all of the museum's objects are on view. The storage contains rock artifacts and is accessible by appointment.

Four Rivers Cultural Center and Museum

676 S.W. 5th Ave.
Ontario, OR 97914
Phone: 541-889-8191
Fax: 541-889-7628
E-mail: info@4rcc.com
URL: www.4rcc.com

☺ Monday – Saturday, 10 a.m. – 5 p.m.

The Four Rivers Cultural Center Museum gathers within its walls more than a century of history. The museum exhibits trace the settlement patterns of the Northern Paiutes as well as Basque, Japanese/Americans, Hispanic, and Euro-American immigrants. The Native element of the collection consists of artifacts from the Sioux, Navajo, Paiute, Haida, and Ancients. Among the collection are artifacts of weaving traditions from the Yurok, Pomo, Eskimos, Apache, Tottonio Odham and Yucca. There is also an extensive collection of lithic objects, including arrow points, atlatl points, knives, scrapers, and drills. Objects from the Northwest include examples from many tribes including Wishram, Makah, Yakama, Quinault, Shushwap, Tlinket, and Klikitat. Pottery from the Southwest Pueblo tribes represents the Zuni, Hopi, Anasazi, and Mogollon. Examples of beads and buckskin are from the Umatilla, Flathead, Wasco, Crow and Wishram tribes.

Portland Art Museum

1219 SW Park Avenue
Portland, OR 97205
Phone: 503-226-2811
Fax: 503-226-4842
E-mail: info@pam.org
URL: web.pam.org/index.asp

☉ **Tuesday, Wednesday, Saturday,
10 a.m. – 5 p.m.; Thursday, Friday,
10 a.m. – 8 p.m.; Sunday, noon – 5 p.m.**

The Portland Art Museum is the oldest art museum in the Pacific Northwest and, since its founding in 1892, it has amassed a diverse collection of more than 33,000 objects and works of art. As the twentieth century dawned, the city of Portland planned for a great extravaganza, the 1905 Lewis and Clark Centennial Exposition. The fair established Portland as a leading West Coast cultural and commercial center. The museum building was constructed with funds from Henry Corbett's bequest and a donation from Mrs. William Sargent Ladd. Families like the Ladds, Corbetts, Failings, Lewises, Hirsches, Adams, Fleischners and Woods were generous lenders, whose holdings included prints, paintings, textiles, sculpture, decorative arts and Native American art. Today's collections are rooted in these early acquisitions.

The 1970s and 1980s saw substantial growth of the museum's collections and programs. In August 2000, the Portland Art Museum celebrated the successful completion of a two-year, $45 million renovation and construction project. Today the museum's collection includes works of European painting and sculpture, American painting and sculpture, English silver, Asian art, Native American art, pre-Columbian art, Cameroon and other African art, contemporary art, sculpture, prints and drawings, and photography.

The Grand Ronde Center for Native American Art designed by Clifford LaFontaine displays some 375 works of art, drawn from virtually every major cultural group in North America, including the Northwest Coast. The museum's collection of Native American art is the most frequently requested aspect of its overall collection and is one of the three most important collections of its type in American art museums. The collection is remarkable for both its depth and diversity, consisting of objects crafted by more than 200 indigenous groups from throughout North America, including prehistoric, historic and contemporary works of outstanding quality.

Oregon

Tribal Art **Museum Collections** *in the* **UNITED STATES**

Museum at Warm Springs

2189 Hwy. 26
Warm Springs, OR 97761
Phone: 541-553 -3331
Fax: 541-553-3338
URL: www.warmsprings.biz/museum

☉ **Daily, 9 a.m. – 5 p.m.**
**Closed Thanksgiving, Christmas and
New Year's Day.**

Opened and dedicated in 1993, the Museum at the Warm Springs Reservation houses the state's single largest collection of Indian artifacts under one roof. The changing exhibition gallery is a flexible venue for the ongoing exploration of every aspect of the Native American experience.

The museum's permanent collection holds an array of over 4,200 objects reflecting centuries of tribal heirlooms that have been passed from generation to generation. Each year the museum's collection grows by accepting artifacts during its annual acquisitions process from enrolled tribal members of Warm Springs. Throughout the year objects are also donated to the museum by outside donors and individuals.

The ethnographical collection contains a wide variety of artifacts. The coiled cedar root baskets and cornhusk bags included are significant evidence of the cultural past and present. There are up to 200 artifacts on display in the permanent exhibit. An ongoing series of changing exhibits also utilizes the permanent collection.

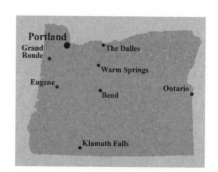

Lelooska Foundation / Cultural Center / Museum

165 Merwin Village Road
Ariel, WA 98603
Phone: 360-225-9522
Fax: 260-225-7416
E-mail: Lelooska_foundation@yahoo.com
URL: www.lelooska.org

⊙ **Saturdays, 11 a.m. – 3 p.m., and by appointment.**

This museum was opened in 1972 by the late Chief Lelooska as an outgrowth of a series of successful living history programs he began in the 1960s relating to Indian life and culture. The collection features more than 600 objects from the Native peoples of North America, most collected by Lelooska and his family. Many of the artifacts were regalia belonging to family members. Some items were traded for by family artisans and others were gifted by close family friends.

Objects of note in the collection include baskets, parfleches, cornhusk bags, dolls, spoons, cradles, moccasins, tomahawks, pipes, pipe bags, fully beaded dresses, a fifteen-foot birch bark canoe, and an entire replica fur trade store, fully furnished to the period.

Virtually all of the artifacts in the collection are on display.

Whatcom Museum of History and Art

121 Prospect Street
Bellingham, WA 98225
Phone: 360-676-6981
URL: www.whatcommuseum.org

⊙ **Tuesday – Sunday, noon – 5 p.m.**

The Whatcom Museum of History & Art occupies four buildings in downtown Bellingham that feature exhibitions on contemporary art and local, state and Northwest Coast history. The museum's collection holds more than 200,000 artifacts of regional importance, including a vast photographic archive.

The history collection reflects the richness and diversity of Pacific Northwest history from post-settlement to the present day. The collection ranges from everyday domestic items to the tools and equipment vital to the agricultural, timber and fishing industries that were prominent in the development of the Northwest.

The art collection's emphasis is on art from the Pacific Northwest, but includes examples of American art from the middle of the nineteenth century to the present.

The ethnology collection's emphasis is on the material culture of the region's indigenous peoples. Here the region is defined as the Pacific Northwest, generally recognized as the area west of the Rocky Mountains from Northern California to Alaska. The collection contains objects of everyday utility as well as artworks used during ceremonial events.

Washington

Cashmere Pioneer Village & Museum

600 Cotlets Way
Cashmere, WA 98815
Phone: 509-782-3230

☺ March 1 – October 31: 9:30 a.m. –
4:30 p.m. November 1 – December 21:
Friday – Sunday, 10:30 a.m. – 3:30 p.m.

This museum is dedicated to the preservation and display of Pacific Northwest history and is owned and operated by the Chelan County Historical Society. The museum displays an extensive archaeological collection from the mid-Columbia River that dates from as early as 9000 years BP. The site also is home to a Pioneer Village with twenty original structures from the area and a railroad installation.

Wanapum Dam Heritage Center

Hwy. 243
Beverly, WA 98823
Phone: 509-754-3541

☺ Monday – Friday, 8:30 a.m. –
4:30 p.m.; Saturday and Sunday,
9 a.m. – 5 p.m.

The recently remodeled Wanapum Heritage Center Museum examines the history of the Wanapum people. The displays are arranged in a chronological sequence that begins in prehistoric times and ends with the construction of Priest Rapids and Wanapum Dams, which dramatically altered the region.

In addition to the museum, a repository is maintained within the Wanapum Heritage Center to provide a secure, climate-controlled environment for Wanapum photographs and artifacts and for archaeological data and collections from the region. The center also includes a Wanapum Traditional Culture Program, designed to perpetuate the people's lifeways, language and traditional material culture. This program recently sponsored the construction of a very large tule mat house.

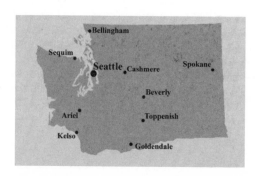

Maryhill Museum of Art

35 Maryhill Museum Drive
Goldendale, WA 98620
Phone: 509-773-3733
Fax: 509-773-6138
E-mail: maryhill@maryhillmuseum.org
URL: www.maryhillmuseum.org

☉ **March 15 – November 15:**
Daily, 9 a.m. – 5 p.m.

The Maryhill Museum of Art has an unusual history, to say the least. Wealthy entrepreneur Samuel Hill bought 6,000 acres overlooking the Columbia River in 1907 and built a state-of-the-art concrete chateau-like mansion on the property. Soon after, his friend Loie Fuller, the noted dancer, convinced him to convert the building to a museum. Though unfinished, the museum was dedicated in 1926 by Queen Marie of Romania, whose country Hill had generously aided after World War I. Following Hill's death in 1931, another friend, Alma Spreckels, a flamboyant San Francisco personality, assumed responsibility for overseeing the completion of the project. She became Maryhill's principal benefactor and donated much of her own art collection to the museum. Under her guidance, the museum opened to the public on Sam Hill's birthday, May 13, 1940.

The museum holds a significant collection of European and American art. It also has Queen Marie's regalia and a full-scale replica of Stonehenge. There is an extensive Native American collection comprised of rare prehistoric rock carvings, intricate baskets and beadwork, and an array of artifacts from throughout North America. The museum has a display of Native American artifacts that closely resemble those Lewis and Clark documented and collected from the Columbia River Gorge area, including a flat bag in the Wasco/Wishxam style that is almost identical to one the explorers acquired while in the area.

Cowlitz County Historical Museum

405 Allen St.
Kelso, WA 98626
Phone: 360-577-3119
URL: www.co.cowlitz.wa.us/museum

☉ **Tuesday – Saturday, 9 a.m. – 5 p.m.;**
Sunday, 1 p.m. – 5 p.m.
Closed on Mondays and holidays.

The Cowlitz County Historical Museum was founded in 1949 to interpret and disseminate the history of Cowlitz County and Southwest Washington. The museum contains an extensive artifact and photograph collection and a large library of materials concerning Cowlitz County.

Local Native American artifacts are a major component of the installation, which also includes a Toutle River settler's log cabin built in 1884, an assortment of decoys, and replicas of a general store, loggers' bunkhouse, steamboat dock, and railroad depot.

Washington

Burke Museum of Natural History and Culture

University of Washington
Seattle, WA 98195-3010
Phone: 206-543-7907
Fax: 206-616-1274
E-mail: recept@u.washington.edu
URL: www.washington.edu/burkemuseum/

☉ **Daily, 10 a.m. – 5 p.m., and until 8 p.m. on the first Thursday of each month.**

Members of the Young Naturalist Society founded this museum and in 1885 erected a building on the University of Washington campus. In 1899 the state legislature designated the museum as the Washington State Museum. In 1962 construction of the current building was made possible through a bequest from the Caroline McGilvra Burke estate in honor of Judge Thomas Burke, a forward-looking Seattle resident who worked to advance understanding among the peoples of the Pacific Rim. The Burke celebrated the opening of a greatly expanded temporary exhibits gallery in June 2005, which will allow it to accommodate larger and more significant traveling exhibits.

The Burke's anthropology division contains two departments, archaeology and ethnology, that hold tribal collections. The archaeology collection includes 500,000 prehistoric objects, primarily of stone and bone, from the Pacific Northwest, including Alaska and British Columbia. It also contains 20,000 historic Native American works, mostly pottery and stone, as well as some material from Mexico and Central and South America. About one-third of the collection was donated by private collectors and the rest is the result of systematic archaeological excavations. The largest private donation was made by Dr. Harold Bergen.

The ethnology collection contains more than 45,000 objects that range from Africa to South America. The most significant portion of the collection is in Native North American materials, some 22,500 objects that include significant works from the Northwest Coast and an encyclopedic collection of baskets. Other objects of note include textiles from Southeast Asia (including Nuosu), Oceanic tapa, storyboards from Palau, and Tibetan thangka paintings.

Less than two percent of the collection is on display. Storage is available to researchers on a limited basis, but the museum is actively working to create a comprehensive online database of its collection.

Seattle Art Museum

100 University Street
Seattle, WA 98101-2902
Phone: 206-654-3100
Fax: 206-654-3135
and
1400 East Prospect Street
Volunteer Park
Seattle, WA 98112-3303
Phone: 206-654-3100
Fax: 206-654-3135
E-mail: webmaster@seattleartmuseum.org
URL: www.seattleartmuseum.org

☉ **The Seattle Art Museum downtown is closed for a major expansion and will reopen Spring 2007.**

Seattle Asian Art Museum:
Tuesday – Sunday, 10 a.m. – 5 p.m.;
Thursday, 10 a.m. – 9 p.m.
Closed Mondays.

For seven decades, the Seattle Art Museum has been a leading visual arts institution in the Pacific Northwest. When the museum opened its doors in 1933, its collection focused primarily on Asian art. The museum moved to a downtown location in 1991 with a new building designed by architect Robert Venturi. Its original location was renovated and reopened as the Seattle Asian Art Museum. Together these museums have matured into a world-class arts institution with a global perspective and a collection that numbers approximately 23,000 objects. In 2004, the museum began a major expansion of the downtown museum, which is presently closed during construction. The first phase of expansion will open in spring 2007.

The Seattle Asian Art Museum features exhibitions of Japanese, Chinese, Korean, Indian, Himalayan, and Southeast Asian art. A lively international center for Asian art and culture, the Seattle Asian Art Museum's holdings rank in the top ten outside of Asia.

The Seattle collection also contains 3,139 objects of African and Oceanic art, 61 Indonesian pieces, and 951 Ancient and Native American objects. Galleries due to open in 2007 will feature new installations of these collections.

The museum's distinctive collection of African art has its foundation in the holdings of the late Katherine White. Her selection of masks and sculpture from many regions of Africa was balanced by an innovative taste for more personal art forms such as textiles, jewelry, furniture, and household objects of East, Central and West Africa. Additional collections of specialized strength include the Christensen Foundation's representation of Kuba art in many media and Simon Ottenberg's selection of Igbo masks. Oceanic holdings are less distinguished but are growing in the area of Philippine and Australian Aboriginal art.

The guiding principle of the installation of Northwest Coast Native art will be the use of Native voices to provide remembrances of past art traditions and art practitioners, an analysis of change, a discussion of the legacy of the older masters, and commentary on the recent "renaissance" of Northwest Coast art.

Washington

Museum and Arts Center in the Sequim-Dungeness Valley

175 West Cedar Street
Sequim, WA 98382
Phone: 360-683-8110
Fax: 360-683-8364
URL: sequimmuseum.org

☉ Tuesdays – Saturdays, 8 a.m. – 4 p.m.

Located in sunny Sequim, Washington, the Museum and Arts Center opened in 1979 and in 1992 it consolidated with the Peninsula Cultural Arts Center forming the Museum & Arts Center in the Sequim-Dungeness Valley. Its mission is to interpret the history of the region, which it does with both natural and cultural exhibits beginning with the first known contact of humans with a mastodon 12,000 years ago as revealed by the Manis Mastodon Excavation. Other exhibits showcase local artists, S'Klallam tribal culture, and pioneer history.

Northwest Museum of Arts and Culture

2316 W. First Avenue
Spokane, WA 99204
Phone: 509-456-3931
E-mail: themac@northwestmuseum.org
URL: www.northwestmuseum.org

☉ Tuesday – Sunday, 11 a.m. – 5 p.m. Open until 9 p.m. on the first Friday of each month. Closed Monday (Except for Martin Luther King, Jr. Day and Presidents Day). Closed Thanksgiving Day, Christmas Day, Easter, Memorial Day, 4th of July, Labor Day.

The Northwest Museum of Arts and Culture collects art, artifacts and primary source material. The collections include over 68,000 objects representing fine art and material culture from the Americas, Europe, and Asia.

The museum represents major regional themes including exploration, settlement, economics, communications, and domestic arts, and includes an extensive textile collection with quilts and clothing from mid-nineteenth century to present. A major interpretive program for the museum is the 1898 Campbell House complex built by mine owner Amasa B. Campbell supported by original furnishings and research documents.

The museum also represents culture groups from throughout the Americas. It holds one of the preeminent collections of Plateau material culture in the United States. Its collection of historic objects is augmented by an archive of more than 10,000 photographic images of Plateau Indian culture. Also included are works by living American Indian artists and artisans of the Plateau.

Museum of Northern British Columbia

100 1st Avenue West
Prince Rupert, BC V8J 3S1
Phone: 250-624-3207
Fax: 250-627-8009
E-mail: mnbc@citytel.net
URL: www.museumofnorthernbc.com

☉ **June – August:**
Monday – Saturday, 9 a.m. – 8 p.m.;
Sunday, 9 a.m. – 5 p.m.
September – May:
Monday – Saturday, 9 a.m. – 5 p.m.

The Museum of Northern British Columbia is built to resemble a Northwest Coast longhouse. Its exhibits portray Northwest Coast history and culture dating back to the end of the last ice age. It emphasizes oral history, archaeological discoveries, and outstanding works of art from antiquity through the present day. It also interprets local settlement and natural history.

Vancouver Museum

1100 Chestnut Street
Vancouver, BC V6J 3J9
Canada
Phone: 604-736-4431
Fax: 604-736-5417
URL: www.vanmuseum.bc.ca

☉ **Tuesday, Wednesday, Friday,**
Saturday, Sunday, 10 a.m. – 5 p.m.;
Thursday, 10 a.m. – 9 p.m.
Closed Mondays.

The Vancouver Museum was founded in 1894 by the Art, Historical and Scientific Association under a banner that invited visitors to view "Paintings and Curios." The museum quickly outgrew its first recorded object, a stuffed trumpeter swan. It moved to the Carnegie Library Building in 1905 and to its present purpose-built location in 1968, having become Canada's largest civic museum.

The museum has hundreds of thousands of artifacts, specimens, and treasures. Areas of particular strength are the Pacific Northwest Coast First Nations collection and the Plains First Nations beadwork collection. There is also a small southeastern Nigerian collection, beadwork and weaponry from East and South Africa, Inuit prints, and bark cloth from Oceania.

British Columbia

Museum of Anthropology at the University of British Columbia

6393 N.W. Marine Drive
Vancouver, B.C. V6T 1Z2
Phone: 604-822-5087
URL: www.moa.ubc.ca

☉ **Winter: Wednesday – Sunday,
11 a.m. – 5 p.m.; Tuesdays to 9 p.m.
Summer: Daily, 10 a.m. – 5 p.m.;
Tuesdays to 9 p.m.**

The University of British Columbia began collecting ethnographic material in 1927. Twenty years later, this material served as the founding collection of the new Museum of Anthropology, which opened in the basement of UBC's main library in 1949. MOA's collections remained in the library until 1976, when they were moved to their current structure designed by renowned Canadian architect Arthur Erickson following Walter and Marianne Koerner's 1975 gift of their extensive Northwest Coast First Nations art collection. Erickson's building is inspired by traditional northern Northwest Coast post-and-beam–style architecture.

The museum houses some 35,000 ethnographic and 500,000 archaeological objects, the majority of which originate from the Northwest Coast of British Columbia. Massive totem poles, carved boxes, bowls, and feast dishes are featured in the museum's Great Hall, while smaller pieces in gold, silver, argillite, wood, ceramic, and other materials are exhibited elsewhere in the galleries.

The museum's extensive Visible Storage System provides public access to approximately 13,000 objects from around the world for comparison and study, as well as for community-based research by artists, elders, students, and others. In addition to First Nations material, the museum also holds significant collections from East and South Asia, the South Pacific, the Americas, Africa, and Europe. Early major donations to MOA include a large collection gathered by F. Burnett of mostly South Pacific materials, which also contained sixty Northwest Coast objects and some archaeological artifacts. The Buttimer Collection of 130 First Nations baskets was also significant.

Important Northwest Coast collections at MOA were acquired through purchase with funds received from H.R. MacMillan. The majority of the over 2,000 objects purchased with MacMillan funds were acquired directly from First Nations families or through First Nations agents in the communities between 1948 and 1965. MacMillan funds also allowed MOA to purchase about fifteen collections of Northwest Coast artifacts assembled by missionaries and others. These include the Rev. G.H. Raley Collection of over 600 objects (1948); the Revs. Collison Collection of almost 200 objects (1960), and the Edith Bevan Cross Collection of almost 700 objects (1962). Both MacMillan and Koerner financed the acquisition of totem poles and other monumental carvings collected as part of the BC Totem Pole Preservation Project in the 1950s, which brought thirty-seven massive carvings to MOA.

Maritime Museum of British Columbia

28 Bastion Square
Victoria, BC V8W 1H9
Canada
Phone: 250-385-4222
Fax: 250-382-2869
URL: www.mmbc.bc.ca

☺ **Daily, 9:30 a.m. – 4:30 p.m. From June 15 – September 15: 9:30 a.m. – 5 p.m. Closed Christmas Day.**

The Maritime Museum of British Columbia is housed in the historic 1889 Provincial Law Courts building situated in Bastion Square.

The three floors of exhibits contain models and artifacts relating to Canada's maritime history. Historical displays discuss the earliest European contacts with the region, including those made by Captain James Cook and George Vancouver, and address the area's territorial see-saw between Russia, the United States and British Canada. A smattering of Native artifacts is incorporated into these displays, but by far the most interesting installation is that of the *Tilikum* (Chinook for "friend"), a three-masted vessel modified from a fifty-year-old, 9.1-meter Native canoe carved from a single cedar log. Captain John Claus Voss and Norman Luxton sailed this unique vessel out of Oak Bay, Victoria, in 1901 intending to circumnavigate the world. The voyage lasted three years, three months, and twelve days and terminated in Margate, England. The vessel was exhibited in London in 1905. It was discovered lying derelict in 1929 and was returned to Victoria by freighter, where restoration was carried out by the Thermopylae Club.

Royal British Columbia Museum

675 Belleville Street
Victoria, BC V8W 9W2
Canada
Phone: 250-356-7226
E-mail: reception@royalbcmuseum.bc.ca
URL: www.royalbcmuseum.bc.ca

☺ **Daily, 9 a.m. – 5 p.m. Closed Christmas Day and New Year's Day.**

The museum was founded in 1886 as the Provincial Museum of Natural History and Anthropology. It was later renamed the British Columbia Provincial Museum and in 1987 became the Royal British Columbia Museum. It houses thousands of historical and contemporary First Nations artifacts as well as ethnographic photographs and audiotapes created throughout British Columbia.

Among the major ethnological collections from the late nineteenth and early twentieth centuries are the Fillip Jacobsen, Charles F. Newcombe and James Teit Collections. In 1978 the museum received a major donation of Haida argillite carvings from the Reif family. Its Potlatch Collection features carvings made by artists in the museum's Carving Program for use in First Nations potlatches and ceremonies. The Mungo Martin House in Thunderbird Park and the Jonathan Hunt House in the First Peoples galleries are versions of historical Kwakwaka'wakw bighouses that continue to have connections with modern First Nations families.

British Columbia

CALIFORNIA
GREATER LOS ANGELES AREA
SANTA FE CRAFTS INC.

*Antique and contemporary
Southwest material; emphasis on
jewelry and Hopi baskets, kachinas.
Wholesale and retail, buying and
selling.*

Barbara Goldeen and John Selmer
PO Box 298
Altadena, CA 91003
Tel: 800-421-7661, 626-398-1789
Fax: 626-398-1575
sfc@mindspring.com
www.santafecrafts.com
☺ *By appointment*

BARAKAT GALLERY

*Extensive range of fine international
antiquities.*

Fayez Barakat
405 North Rodeo Dr.
Beverly Hills, CA 90210
Tel: 310-859-8408
Fax: 310-276-1346
barakat@barakatgallery.com
www.barakatgallery.com
☺ *Monday – Saturday, 10 a.m. – 6 p.m.; or
by appointment*

VANISHING INDIAN

*Silver Native jewelry, pottery, and
more; contemporary and antique.
Repairs of some Native material.*

Connie Smith
233 S. Victory Blvd.
Burbank, CA 91502
Tel: 818-846-7570
☺ *Monday – Saturday, 10:30 a.m. – 5 p.m.*

TRIBAL TREASURES

*Kuba textiles, art and artifacts,
Toma fetishes; antique and contemporary.*

Tekla M. Morgan
6151 Canterbury Dr. #109
Culver City, CA 90230
Tel: 310-670-1271
Fax: 310-670-1271
tribaltreasures@comcast.net
☺ *By appointment*

MAHAMADOU SYLLA

African art
16643 Nanberry Rd.
Encino, CA 91436
Tel: 818-788-1163
Cell: 310-497-9913
Fax: 818-230-1284
☺ *By appointment*

THE TURQUOISE HUT

*Native American jewelry, artifacts,
pottery, rugs, baskets, paintings;
antique and contemporary.*

Paul Trevizo
321 N. Verdugo Rd.
Glendale, CA 91206
Tel: 818-243-1001
turquoisehut@sbcglobal.net
www.turquoisehut.com
☺ *Monday – Saturday, 11 a.m. – 6 p.m.*

AFRICA AND MORE

*High-quality African tribal art and
ethnographica, ancient and antique
international beads*

Judith Harris
1045 8th Street
Hermosa Beach, CA 90254
Tel: 310-376-1227
info@africaandmore.com
www.africaandmore.com
☺ *By appointment*

ANTHROPOS FINE ART

North American Indian and pre-Columbian art, primarily from the West Coast regions. Old World Antiquities. Appraisal, consultation, acquisition, and deacquisition services.

Ronald D. Normandeau
860 Glenneyre Street, suite #2
Laguna Beach, CA 92651
Tel: 800-243-2138
Fax: 949-443-4120
info@anthroposgallery.com
www.anthroposgallery.com
☺ *By appointment*

CONRAD ANGONE

Full range of North American, Canadian, and Alaskan Native material
PO Box 27665
Los Angeles, CA 90027
Tel: 323-664-9756
artamerind@aol.com
☺ *By appointment*

JAN BAUM GALLERY

Celebrating the best contemporary art from Los Angeles, New York, and points east and west for 29 years. Tribal arts have always been the rich accompaniment, with the accent on African art.

Jan Baum
170 S. La Brea Ave.
Los Angeles, CA 90036
Tel: 323-932-0170
Fax: 323-932-0245
art@janbaum.com
www.janbaum.com
☺ *Tuesday – Saturday, 10 a.m. – 5:30 p.m.*

DIMONDSTEIN TRIBAL ARTS

African tribal art
Joshua Dimondstein
749 Longwood Avenue
Los Angeles, CA 90005
Tel: 415-613-2021
info@africantribalart.com
www.africantribalart.com
☺ *By appointment*

HIGH NOON WESTERN COLLECTIBLES

Western collectibles, cowboy and Indian material, Indian rugs and beadwork, Mexican collectibles
Danny Verrier
9929 Venice Blvd.
Los Angeles, CA 90034
Tel: 310-202-9010
danny@highnoon.com
www.highnoon.com
☺ *By appointment*

LACY PRIMITIVE AND FINE ART

Tribal and Abstract Expressionist art from the modern school.
Vanna and Lee Lacy
1240 Sierra Alta Way
Los Angeles, CA 90069
Tel: 310-271-0807
Info@lacyprimitiveandfineart.com
www.lacyprimitiveandfineart.com
☺ *Tuesday – Saturday, 11 a.m. – 5 p.m.; and by appointment*

PRIMARY SOURCE

Antique tribal art.
John Strusinski
4847 W. Jefferson Blvd.
Los Angeles, CA 90016
Tel: 323-732-6131
info@primarysourcearts.com
☺ *By appointment*

Tribal Art in **WESTERN NORTH AMERICA**

Tribal Art in **WESTERN NORTH AMERICA**

LESLIE SACKS FINE ART

Contemporary art, African and Asian art

Leslie Sacks
11640 San Vicente Blvd.
Los Angeles, CA 90066
Tel: 310-820-9448
www.lesliesacks.com
☺ *Monday – Saturday, 10 a.m. – 6 p.m.*

JERRY SOLOMON ASIAN & TRIBAL ARTS

Japanese masks and sculpture; arms and armor; African, Oceanic, Indonesian, and Philippine tribal arts.

Jerry Solomon
PO Box 48737
Los Angeles, CA 90048
Tel: 323-876-2183
jsolomon@earthlink.net
www.jerrysolomon.com
☺ *By appointment*

MICHAEL SORAFINE PRIMITIVE ARTS

Quality tribal artifacts from Africa, Indonesia, and Oceania.

Michael Sorafine
Los Angeles, CA
Tel: 323-930-1822
Fax: 323-931-9563
mspa.la@ispwest.com
☺ *By appointment*

STENDAHL GALLERY

Pre-Columbian art.

Ronald Damman
7065 Hillside Ave.
Los Angeles, CA 90068
Tel: 323-876-7740
Fax: 323-876-2143
stendahlart@aol.com
☺ *By appointment*

TURKANA PRIMITIVE ARTS / ERNIE WOLFE GALLERY

Contemporary African and antique tribal art

Ernie and Diane Wolfe
1655 Sawtelle Blvd.
Los Angeles, CA 90025
Tel: 310-478-2960
Fax: 310-473-7672
☺ *By appointment*

KENT WATTERS

Indonesian textiles and artifacts
10573 West Pico Blvd. #36
Los Angeles, CA 90064
Tel: 310-403-0503 (Los Angeles)/
011-62-8123-997733 (Bali)
www.ata-la.com/
kentwatters/index.htm
☺ *By appointment*

OCEANIC TRIBAL ART

Oceanic and African tribal art.
Edward Glauder
Malibu, CA
Tel: 310-457-1112
glauder@oceanictribalart.com
www.oceanictribalart.com
☺ *By appointment*

MARK A. JOHNSON ASIAN & TRIBAL ART

Tribal art from Southeast Asia and the Western Pacific Islands
Mark A. Johnson
578 Washington Blvd. #555
Marina Del Rey, CA 90292
Tel: 800-923-1653
asiaart@markajohnson.com
www.markajohnson.com
☺ *By appointment*

MICHAEL HAMSON OCEANIC ART

Fine traditional art from New Guinea and the Pacific.

Michael R. Hamson
844 Rincon Lane
Palos Verdes Estates, CA 90274
Tel: 310-373-1392
Cell: 310-619-4562
mhamson@verizon.net
www.michaelhamson.com
☺ *By appointment*

JIM CONLEY ETHNIC ART

Ethnographic art and collectibles
Jim Conley
PO Box 1297
Redondo Beach, CA 90278
Tel: 310-538-1740
jgconley@mac.com
☺ *By appointment*

MOUNTAIN LION TRADING POST

Antique Northern American Indian art, pre-Columbian art, African and Oceanic art.

Steve Nelson
304A Vista Del Mar
Redondo Beach, CA 90277
Tel: 310-375-3160
☺ *By appointment*

TONY BERLANT AMERIND ART, INC.

Navajo blankets and early sand-painting rugs; kachina dolls and Mimbres ceramics; early man stone tools. Advice.

Tony Berlant
1304 12th St.
Santa Monica, CA 90401
Tel: 310-395-5678
tony@berlant.net
☺ *By appointment*

HISTORIA

Spanish colonial and pre-Columbian art
James and Sidsie Caswell
1322 2nd St. #2
Santa Monica, CA 90401
Tel: 310-394-3384
info@historia-antiques.com
www.historia-antiques.com
☺ *Tuesday – Saturday, 11 a.m. – 6:30 p.m.; or by appointment.*

FAIRMONT TRADING COMPANY

Pre-1940's Southwest Indian jewelry, California baskets, and historic pottery. Will lecture on origins of Southwest Indian silverwork, appraise, and judge competitions.

Jim and Lauris Phillips
PO Box 689
South Pasadena, CA 91031
Fax only: 626-796-3820
laurphil@earthlink.net
☺ *By appointment only*

INDIAN ART CENTER OF CALIFORNIA

Navajo rugs, jewelry, pottery, sandpaintings, kachina, and artifacts.
12666 Ventura Blvd.
Studio City, CA 91604
Tel: 818-763-3430
☺ *Monday – Saturday, 10 a.m. – 5:30 p.m.*

EAGLE'S NEST GALLERY AND TRADING POST

Native American and Western goods; antique and contemporary
135 N. 2nd Ave.
Upland, CA 91786
Tel: 909-981-4897
☺ *Tuesday – Friday, 10 a.m. – 5 p.m.; Saturday, 10 a.m. – 6 p.m.; Thanksgiving – Christmas: Sunday, noon – 5 p.m.*

Tribal Art in **WESTERN NORTH AMERICA**

PHILIP GARAWAY NATIVE AMERICAN ART

Antique Native American art, vintage Western paintings, Navajo weavings, Pueblo pottery, basketry, kachinas, beadwork, Inuit, etc.

Philip Garaway
PO Box 1020
Venice, CA 90291
Tel: 310-577-8555
philipgaraway@earthlink.net
☺ *By appointment*

LEONARD KALINA FINE ARTS

Pre-Columbian art

Leonard Kalina
974A Indiana Ave
Venice, CA 90291
Tel: 310-399-0136
lekalina@earthlink.net
☺ *By appointment*

K.R. MARTINDALE GALLERY

American Indian and world art. Consultation on special events and seminars.

Kim R. Martindale
1154 Grant Ave.
Venice, CA 90291
Tel: 310-822-9145
Fax: 310-822-9179
krmartindale@mac.com
www.krmartindale.com
☺ *By appointment*

SORAKATA SYLLA

African art
19953 Ingomar St.
Winnetka, CA 91306
Tel: 818-709-3715
Cell: 818-968-8516
sorakatasylla@sbcglobal.net
☺ *By appointment*

SAN FRANCISCO BAY AREA
RUTH BELIKOVE

19th- and 20th-century blankets, Navajo and Rio Grande rugs, Pueblo pottery. Particular interest in Teec Nos Pos rugs woven prior to WWII.
98 Steuben Bay
Alameda, CA 94502
Tel: 510-522-3021
Fax: 510-522-3021
ruth@belikove.com
www.belikove.com
☺ *By appointment*

TODOS SANTOS TRADING POST

Native American artifacts—buying, selling, and trading

Donald Phelps
105 Muir Lane
Alamo, CA 94507
Tel: 925-837-4996
phelpststp@sbcglobal.net
☺ *By appointment*

GEORGIA SALES

Asian and Indonesian art
P.O. Box 587
Belvedere, CA 94920
Tel: 415-435-0735
Fax: 415-435-0839
selasag@sbcglobal.net
☺ *By appointment*

ETHNIC ARTS

Contemporary and antique tribal art and textiles and jewelry

Eleanor Hopewell
1314 Tenth Street
Berkeley, CA 94710
Tel: 510-527-5270
info@ethnicarts.com
www.ethnicarts.com
☺ *Monday – Saturday, 11 a.m. – 6 p.m.; Sunday noon – 5 p.m.*

JOYCE HULBERT TAPESTRY AND TEXTILE RESTORATION

Specializing in conservation mounting, custom dyeing, and exhibition preparation.
Joyce Hulbert
Berkeley, CA
Tel: 510-845-0825
textileart@sbcglobal.net
☺ *By appointment*

RICHARD KIBSGAARD

Antiquities, Native American material, and California photographs
PO Box 4382
Berkeley, CA 94704
Tel: 510-841-0640
rkibsgaard@aol.com
☺ *By appointment*

ANDRES MORAGA

Antique textiles and works of art from Africa, South America, Oceania, Southeast Asia, and especially Andean traditions (Mpuche). Mbuti paintings, Kuba textiles, early fiber art, headdresses, basketry, beadwork.
Berkeley, CA
Tel: 510-527-2556
moraga@lmi.net
www.sftribal.com/Andres-Moraga
☺ *By appointment*

NORTHERN CORDILLERA IMPORTS

Highland Philippine ethnographica
Armand Cating
37 Fairway Dr.
Daly City, CA 94015
Tel: 925-360-2977
pasiking@gmail.com
www.pasiking.com
☺ *By appointment*

MYSTERY DANCE

Antique Himalayan art.
Artist, collector, and dealer
Mort Golub
PO Box 710
Corte Madera, CA 94976
Tel: 415-927-3814
mort@mysterydance.com
www.mysterydance.com
www.himalayanmasks.com
☺ *By appointment*

JERRY WEISBERG TRIBAL ANTIQUES

Native American art and South Pacific tribal art
Jerry Weisberg
7908 Potrero Ave.
El Cerrito, CA 94530
Tel: 510-232-8683
merugman@aol.com
eBay store: Jerry Weisberg Tribal Arts
☺ *By appointment*

INSULINDE INDONESIAN ARTS

Antique Indonesian sculpture, textiles, and gold
Frank Wiggers
P.O. Box 764
Forest Knolls, CA 94933
Tel: 415-488-0599
Cell: 415-609-5313
insulinde@aol.com
☺ *By appointment*

MICHAEL HOUGH

Arrowheads and lithic materials, baskets, beadwork, pottery, pre-Columbian material.
Los Gatos, CA 95032
Tel: 408-885-5441, 408-358-0405
chiefbluebone@comcast.net
☺ *By appointment*

Tribal Art in WESTERN NORTH AMERICA

XANADU GALLERY

Art and antiques from Asia, ethnographic arts from Oceania, and pre-Columbian antiquities. Second location in San Francisco.

871 Santa Cruz Ave.
Menlo Park, CA 94025
Tel: 650-329-9999
info@xanadugallery.us
www.xanadugallery.us
☺ *Tuesday – Saturday, 10 a.m. – 6 p.m.*

MIRANDA CRIMP TRIBAL & ASIAN ART

Antique Indonesian jewelry, textiles, beads, baskets, and sculpture

Miranda Crimp
Mill Valley, CA 94941
Tel: 415-388-8072
mirandacrimp@yahoo.com
www.sftribal.com/Miranda-Crimp
☺ *By appointment*

THOMAS MURRAY ASIATICA– ETHNOGRAPHICA

Museum-quality Indonesian tribal sculpture and textiles; art from India, Southeast Asia, Tibet, China, and Japan.

Thomas Murray
775 E. Blithedale #321
Mill Valley, CA 94941
Tel: 415-332-3445
tmurray@well.com
www.asianart.com/thomasmurray
☺ *By appointment*

VICKI SHIBA

Asian and tribal art
P.O. Box 2255
Mill Valley, CA 94941
Tel: 415-383-6995
shibart@pacbell.net
☺ *By appointment*

RYANN WILLIS AFRICAN ART

African art, specializing in terracottas

Ryann Willis
San Francisco Bay Area
Tel: 415-383-9560
ryann@ryannwillis.com
www.ryannwillis.com
☺ *By appointment*

AMERICAN INDIAN ART

Antique Native American art and artifacts

Frank Steward
PO Box 115
Larkspur, CA 94977
Tel: 415-892-7816
buddhaaaaa@aol.com
☺ *By appointment only*

FRED W. KING NATIVE AMERICAN ART

Navajo weavings from classic blankets to regional rugs. Early and traditional Navajo and Pueblo jewelry.

Fred W. King
448 Ignacio Boulevard #241
Novato, CA 94949
Tel: 415-456-8239
☺ *By appointment*

JOHN RISTOW GALLERY

Greek, Roman, Egyptian and Celtic antiquities, pre-Columbian and African art

John Ristow
PO Box 909
Novato, CA 94948
Tel: 415-898-1185
Cell: 415-328-0061
jristow2@earthlink.net
☺ *By appointment*

McCUE

Antique African art

Scott McCue
83 Orinda Way
Orinda, CA 94563
Tel/Fax: 925-253-1719
info@mccuetribalart.com
www.mccuetribalart.com
☺ *By appointment*

HIMALAYAN TRIBAL ART

Tribal and ritual art from the Himalayas

Robert Brundage
40 4th St., #242
Petaluma, CA 94952
Tel: 707-793-9662
rb@artyeti.com
www.artyeti.com
☺ *By appointment*

DAVE DEROCHE

Antique arts of Africa, Oceania and the Americas, including pre-Columbian. Buying and representing entire old collections.

2083 Oakland Ave
Piedmont, CA 94611
Tel: 510-654-0400
dave@galleryderoche.com
www.galleryderoche.com
☺ *By appointment*

GUILLERMINA

Asian arts and antiques; specialty in Japanese mingei and Japanese textiles; Thai and Burmese material

109-111 W. Richmond Ave.
Point Richmond, CA 94801
Tel: 510-237-0036
guillermina@guillermina.com
www.guillermina.com
☺ *Wednesday – Saturday, noon – 6 p.m.; and by appointment*

ZENA KRUZICK TRIBAL ART

Artifacts, textiles, and jewelry from Africa, Oceania, Indonesia, and Asia.

Zena Kruzick
P.O. Box 284, Station A
Richmond, CA 94808
Tel/Fax: 510-236-6848
zena@zkta.com
www.zenakruzick.com
☺ *By appointment*

GARY SPRATT FINE ART

Native American, Oceanic art, American painting, and related rare books. Sales, appraisals and consultation.

Gary Spratt
P.O. Box 162
Rutherford, CA 94573
Tel: 707-963-4022
Fax: 707-963-1742
garycspratt@yahoo.com
www.garysprattfineart.com
☺ *By appointment*

ANTONIO'S ANTIQUES

Fine European and American period furnishings and Native American basketry collection

Paul Novak
701 Bryant Street
San Francisco, CA 94107
Tel: 415-781-1737
Fax: 415-243-9227
antoniosantiques@msn.com
www.antoniosantiques.com
☺ *Monday – Friday, 8:30 a.m. – 5 p.m.; Saturday, 10 a.m. – 3 p.m.*

Tribal Art in WESTERN NORTH AMERICA

ARTE TEXTIL

Ancient textiles and objects from South America.

Steve Berger
San Francisco, CA
Tel: 415-753-0342
Fax: 415-753-1346
sberg753@aol.com
☺ *By appointment*

JAMES BLACKMON GALLERY

Antique textiles - Near East, Central Asia, South America, Africa. Appraisals, cleaning, and conservation

James W. Blackmon
2140 Bush St., #1
San Francisco, CA 94115
Tel: 415-922-1859
Fax: 415-922-0406
jwb111@pacbell.net
www.cloudband.com
☺ *By appointment*

CHARLES CAMPBELL GALLERY

Contemporary California and Bay Area painting and sculpture; retablos, Spanish colonial, pre-Columbian, Native American, Indian miniatures

Charles Campbell and Steven Lopez
645 Chestnut St.
San Francisco, CA 94133
Tel: 415-441-8680
ccgalry@pacbell.net
www.charlescampbellgallery.com
☺ *Tuesday – Friday, 11 a.m. – 5 p.m.; Saturday, noon – 4 p.m.; and by appointment.*

COLONIAL ARTS

Fine Spanish colonial art, Mexican retablos, santos, ceramics, tribal art and textiles

James Eddy, III
463 Union St.
San Francisco, CA 94133
Tel: 415-505-0680
colonialarts@aol.com
www.colonialarts.com
☺ *Tuesday – Saturday, 11 a.m. – 5 p.m.*

ROBERT DOWLING TRIBAL ART

Pre-Columbian and tribal art. Appraisal and consultation services.

Robert Dowling
San Francisco, CA
Tel: 415-279-0032
RDowling@TribalAntiques.com
www.TribalAntiques.com
☺ *By appointment*

DREAMING ROOM

African, Asian, the Americas, Oceanic; contemporary and antique

Robert Hemphill
245 Columbus Avenue
San Francisco, CA 94133
Tel: 415-788-7882
dreamingroom@yahoo.com
www.dreamingroom.com
☺ *Wed.– Thu., 7 – 11 p.m.; Fri., 7 p.m. – 12; Sat., 4 p.m. – 12; Sun., 4 p.m. – 9 p.m.*

DAVID HOWARD

Southeast Asia: Filipino, Indonesian, Burmese, and Thai.

49 Rivoli
San Francisco, CA 94117
Tel: 415-664-4699
International: 011-666-0749441
info@artsalesandrentals.com
www.artsalesandrentals.com
☺ *By appointment*

HYDE & SEEK ANTIQUES

Native American and Mexican folk art – Collecting for 21 years

Anne Kaufman
1913 Hyde St.
San Francisco, CA 94109
Tel: 415-776-8865
Fax: 415-931-0915
sfhydeandseek@aol.com
☺ *Wednesday – Sunday; or by appointment*

LARRY JOHNSON'S ANTIQUES

Folk art, Native American and pre-Columbian art, ephemera

Larry Johnson
733 Congo Street
San Francisco, CA 94131
Tel: 415-587-3689, 415-584-4409
larryjohnson33@earthlink.net
☺ *By appointment*

TONY KITZ ORIENTAL CARPETS

Antique carpets and textiles, focusing on tribal and village weavings

Tony Kitz
2843 Clay Street
San Francisco, CA 94115
Tel: 415-346-2100
Fax: 415-346-3548
tonykitzrugs@yahoo.com
www.tonykitzrugs.com
☺ *Monday – Friday, 10 a.m. – 6 p.m.;
Saturday, 10 a.m. – 5 p.m.*

STEVEN R. KROLIK

Collector and dealer, ethnographic research, consultation, appraisal, lectures and presentations.

400 Locust St., suite 1
San Francisco, CA 94118
Tel: 415-346-0450
Fax: 415-921-6698
☺ *By appointment*

ELAYNE MARQUIS

Pre-Columbian and tribal art
2299 Pacific Ave. #71
San Francisco, CA 94115
Tel: 415-567-1575
Fax: 415-567-1575
elaynemarq@aol.com
☺ *By appointment*

WALT MOREAU

Pre-1900 Plains Indian art, American Indian beadwork and weapons
PO Box 14764
San Francisco, CA 94114
Tel: 415-861-8319
Cell: 415-531-2342
wmoreau130@aol.com
www.moreau.com
☺ *By appointment*

DAVID F. ROSENTHAL

Oceanic art and related books
2158 Sutter Street
San Francisco, CA 94115
Tel: 415-922-8978
dfr@oceanic-art.net
www.oceanic-art.net
☺ *By appointment*

SONGLINES ABORIGINAL ART

Contact period through contemporary Aboriginal art
David Betz
San Francisco, CA
Tel: 415-871-5901
curator@aboriginal-art.com
www.aboriginal-art.com
☺ *By appointment*

Tribal Art in WESTERN NORTH AMERICA

TWIGA

African art and jewelry design
3333 Sacramento Street
San Francisco, CA 94118
Tel: 415-292-8020
twigasf@yahoo.com
www.twigagallery.com
☺ *Monday – Saturday, 11 a.m. – 6 p.m.;*
Sunday by appointment

JAMES WILLIS TRIBAL ART

African, Oceanic, and Indonesian tribal art
James Willis
1637 Taylor Street
San Francisco, CA 94133
Tel; 415-885-6736
Fax: 415-885-6721
tribalart@jameswillis.com
☺ *By appointment*

XANADU GALLERY

Art and antiques from Asia, ethnographic arts from Oceania, and pre-Columbian amtiquities.
140 Maiden Lane
San Francisco, CA 94108
Tel: 415-392-9999
info@xanadugallery.us
www.xanadugallery.us
☺ *Tuesday – Saturday, 10 a.m.– 6 p.m.*

FARROW FINE ART GALLERY

Antique tribal weapons and ethnic art
Erik Farrow
19 Lovell Avenue
San Rafael, CA 94901
Tel: 415-485-0803
Cell: 415-717-5588
farrow@eriksedge.com
www.eriksedge.com
☺ *By appointment*

INDOARTS, INC.

Providing for purchase antique, collectible and new textiles, Buddhist art, ephemera, books, beads, and jewelry from SE Asia and Indonesia with attention to our clients' special requests
Noeleke Glenn Klavert
3424 Sacramento St.
San Francisco, 94118
Tel: 415-922-5131
also
PO Box 151357
San Rafael, CA 94915
Tel: 415-453-1896
Cell: 415-602-8753
Fax: 415-453-1896
indotextiles@yahoo.com
www.indoartssf.com
☺ *By appointment*

TONY ANNINOS

Ethnographic jewelry, Himalayan art, Oriental rugs and textiles
3020 Bridgeway, PMB 151
Sausalito, CA 94965
Tel: 415-331-1573
Fax: 415-331-5356
tonyanninos@yahoo.com
☺ *By appointment*

SUMMERHOUSE ANTIQUES

"Old and unusual Pueblo pottery" - specializing in Southwestern pottery
Carol and Allan Hayes
4000 Bridgeway, suite 313
Sausalito, CA 94965
Tel: 415-332-3489
Fax: 415-332-2577
summerhouseantiques@gmail.com
☺ *By appointment and at shows*

ELSEWHERE IN CALIFORNIA
TRIBALMANIA.COM

Oceanic, Philippine, Aboriginal, African, Asian, Indonesian, American art
Michael Auliso
PO Box 757
Ben Lomond, CA 95005
(near Santa Cruz)
Tel/Fax: 831-336-3015
sales@tribalmania.com
www.tribalmania.com
☺ _By appointment_

PICARD TRADE BEAD MUSEUM & AFRICAN ART GALLERY

African trade beads found in Africa, African art and textiles
John and Ruth Picard
27885 Berwick Drive
Carmel, CA 93923
Tel: 831-625-7108
info@picardbeads.com
www.picardbeads.com
☺ _By appointment_

GENE QUINTANA

Native American basketry
PO Box 533
Carmichael, CA 95609
Tel: 916-485-8232
vipbasketman@aol.com
☺ _By appointment_

THOMAS JOHN ERHARDT

Huichol art, Mexican masks, Indian and Mexican textiles, pre-Columbian material.
275 Orange Ave., unit 202
Chula Vista, CA 91911
Tel: 619-498-1705
thomas@latinamericanfolkart.com
www.latinamericanfolkart.com
☺ _By appointment_

H & P GALLERY

Antique American Indian basketry
Bob Hickman
7137 Brayton Ave.
Citrus Heights, CA 95621
Tel: 916-996-3196
roberthhickman@earthlink.net
☺ _By appointment_

SOUTHWESTERN INDIAN DEN

Museum-quality handmade Native American art; antique and contemporary
Jackie Jones
1201 1st St., suite 104
Coronado, CA 92118
Tel: 619-435-3561
swid1@netzero.com
www.southwesternindianart.com
☺ _Daily, 10 a.m. – 6 p.m._

APPLEBY INTERNATIONAL ARTS

Tribal textiles and art from Asia and the Americas.
Jeff Appleby
9814 Carson Place
Escondido, CA 92029
Tel: 760-233-0404
jean@jeanshandwovens.com
☺ _Weekdays, 11 a.m. – 5 p.m. (call first); weekends by appointment_

INDIAN-WEST EMPORIUM

Basketry, regalia, Northern California Indian art; antique and contemporary.
Linda and Rene Vit
326 2nd St.
Eureka, CA 95501
Tel: 707-442-3042
indianwest@yahoo.com
☺ _Monday – Sunday, 10:30 a.m. – 6 p.m._

Tribal Art in WESTERN NORTH AMERICA

Tribal Art in **WESTERN NORTH AMERICA**

JOHN C. RAUZY

Antique American Indian basketry, weavings, and beadwork
PO Box 83
Folsom, CA 95763
Tel: 916-988-8993
srauzy@aol.com
☺ *By appointment*

AMERICAN INDIAN SHOP

Full range of American Indian material with an emphasis on basketry; antique and contemporary.
Leon and Bryan Taylor
4787 North Blackstone Ave.
Fresno, CA 93726
Tel: 559-224-8312
Fax: 559-224-8310
amerindianshop@yahoo.com
☺ *Monday – Saturday, 10 a.m.– 5:30 p.m.*

C. DOUGLAS & MARILYNN GUSKE

Indian and Western Americana
PO Box 12951
Fresno, CA 93779
Tel: 559-226-3588
cdg4indian@aol.com
☺ *By appointment*

AFRICA AND BEYOND

Authentic traditional and contemporary African art
Ian Allen
1250 Prospect St.
La Jolla, CA 92037
Tel: 800-422-3742
and 858-454-9983
sales@africaandbeyond.com
www.africaandbeyond.com
☺ *Daily, 10:30 a.m. – 6 p.m.*

PEREGRINE GALLERIES

Early material - California paintings, Taxco and Native American jewelry, Miriam Haskell, Jensen. Second location in Santa Barbara.
Marlene Vitanza
1133 Coast Village Road
Montecito, CA 93108
Tel: 805-969-9673
mperegrine@aol.com
www.peregrinegalleries.com
☺ *Daily, noon – 5:30 p.m.*

PAUL'S INDIAN STORE

Authentic Navajo rugs, jewelry, pottery, baskets.
1725 East F St.
Oakdale, CA 95361
Tel: 209-847-8763
sales@paulsindian.com
www.paulsindian.com
☺ *Daily, 9 a.m. – 5 p.m.*

RAE NEUMEN, A PRIVATE GALLERY

Spanish colonial art of the 17th – early 20th century; some contemporary Mexican folk art
Rae and Joe Neumen
854 West Highland Ave.
Redlands, CA 92373
Tel: 909-798-3534
jneumen@verizon.net
☺ *By appointment*

PRESIDIO JEWELRY & PAWN

Quality Native American material - authentic, unusual, and antique
Dan Harlan
3555 Rosecrans #105A
San Diego, CA 92110
Tel: 619-275-3494
☺ *Monday – Friday, 10 a.m. – 5 p.m.;*
Saturday, 10 a.m. – 4 p.m.

ARTS OF THE ASMAT

Asmat art and artifacts, art from the Mamasa Poraja area.

Phyllis Hischier
4810 Coyote Canyon Rd.
San Luis Obispo, CA 93401
Tel: 805-801-3665
hischier@earthlink.net
www.asmat-art.net
☺ By appointment

PEREGRINE GALLERIES

Early Native American baskets, beadwork, weavings; American and European paintings. Second location in Montecito.

Marlene Vitanza
508 Brinkerhoff St.
Santa Barbara, CA 93101
Tel: 805-963-3134
mperegrine@aol.com
www.peregrinegalleries.com
☺ Monday – Saturday, 10 a.m. – 5 p.m.

CLEAR SKY

Full range of antique North American Indian material, specializing in baskets and Navajo and Southwest textiles

Russell Kloer
Sonoma, CA 95476
Tel: 707-939-1115
russell@clearsky.net
☺ By appointment

JEROME EVANS

Antique and contemporary art of the native peoples of Oceania, Africa, and North and South America

P.O. Box 7101
South Lake Tahoe, CA 96158
Tel: 530-541-3450
jevansattahoe@aol.com
www.jeromeevans.net
☺ By appointment

MARION HAMILTON GALLERY

Spanish 17th – 19th century art, African, Central Asian textiles

Marion Hamilton
304 Railroad Ave
Winters, CA 95694
Tel: 530-795-3707
marion304@hotmail.com
www.marionhamilton.com
☺ Wednesday – Sunday, 11 a.m. – 5 p.m.

OREGON
AMERICAN TRAILS

Native American, Western, and wildlife
27 N. Main Street
Ashland, OR 97520
Tel: toll free 877-587-2455, 541-488-2731
cs@americantrails.com
www.americantrails.com
☺ Summer: Daily, 10 a.m. – 8 p.m.; Winter: Daily, 10 a.m. – 6 p.m.

JOHN BARKER

Textiles and ethnographic arts of Asia.
PO Box 3146
Ashland, OR 97520
Tel: 541-488-6985
jbarts@ccountry.net
☺ By appointment

HEIDI BECKER ANTIQUES

Plains and Plateau beadwork a speciality. Basketry, Zuni and Navajo jewelry; Native American photographs and postcards. Appraisals and consultations, buying and selling.

Heidi Becker
Eugene, OR
Tel: 541-485-5887
hbecker52@msn.com
☺ By appointment

Tribal Art in **WESTERN NORTH AMERICA**

Tribal Art in WESTERN NORTH AMERICA

DARLENE D. FREDRICK

Basketry, Plateau bags and bead-work. Appraisals and consultations.
2465 Marylhaven Pl.
Lake Oswego, OR 97034
Tel: 503-697-5117
darlenefredrick@aol.com
☺ *By appointment*

ARTHUR W. ERICKSON, INC.

Old Native American baskets, bead-work, stone sculpture from the Columbia River area. Appraisal services.
Arthur W. Erickson
1030 SW Taylor
Portland, OR 97205
Tel: 503-227-4710
Fax: 503-279-9146
arthur@arthurwerickson.com
www.arthurwerickson.com
☺ *Wednesdays, by appointment*

QUINTANA GALLERIES

Indigenous art – Northwest Coast, Arctic, contemporary, baskets, bead-work, pottery, kachinas, vintage photography
120 N.W. Ninth Ave.
Portland, OR 97209
Tel: 800-321-1729, 503-223-1729
director@quintanagalleries.com
www.quintanagalleries.com
☺ *Tuesday – Saturday, 10:30 a.m.– 5:30 p.m.*

WASHINGTON
RUDI SOUTH

Asian and Southeast Asian classical and tribal art
Dan Cook
6717 NE Marshall Rd.
Bainbridge Island, WA 98110
Tel: 206-842-4344

dan@rudisouth.com
www.rudisouth.com
☺ *By appointment*

PLAINS PACIFIC GALLERY

Historic Plateau art, beadwork, cornhusk bags, flat bags, Northwest basketry and textiles, Pueblo pottery, and California basketry. Northwest Coast and Columbia River objects. Seeking to purchase quality objects.
Kyle M. Ward
PO Box 1690
Castle Rock, WA 98611
Tel: 360-274-7363
k.ward@prodigy.net
www.plainspacificgallery.com
☺ *Wednesday – Saturday, 11 a.m. – 3:30 p.m.; or by appointment*

PETER-MICHAEL BOYD

Traditional African art and material culture.
343 N. 104th St.
Seattle, WA 98133
Tel/Fax: 206-297-3184
petermichael.boyd@att.net
☺ *By appointment*

FLURY & CO. LTD

Vintage photography of Edward Curtis
Lois Flury
Tel: 206-587-0260

JACKSON STREET GALLERY

Antique Native American objects
James Flury
322 First Avenue S.
Seattle, WA 98104
Tel: 206-407-0102
curtis@fluryco.com
www.fluryco.com
☺ *Monday – Saturday, 11 a.m. – 6 p.m.*

BURTON L. HOLT

Philippine tribal artifacts and textiles
1704 First Ave. North
Seattle, WA 98109
Tel/Fax: 206-282-3661
burtonlholt@yahoo.com
☺ *By appointment*

KIBO GALERIE

Traditional African art
Lucien Guenneguez
323 Occidental Ave. South
Seattle, WA 98104
Tel: 206-442-2100
kibogalerie@qwest.net
www.kibogalerie.com
☺ *Tuesday – Saturday, 11 a.m. – 5 p.m.*

LEGACY LTD.

Historic and contemporary
Northwest Coast Indian and Eskimo
art
Paul Nicholson
1003 1st Ave.
Seattle, WA 98104
Tel: 206-624-6350
legacy@drizzle.com
www.thelegacyltd.com
☺ *Monday – Saturday, 10 a.m. – 6 p.m.*

LEWIS/WARA GALLERY

Fine Oceanic art.
Kirby Kallas-Lewis
1121 15th Ave.
Seattle, WA 98122
Tel: 206-405-4355
Fax: 206-405-1584
gallery@lewiswara.com
www.lewiswara.com
☺ *By appointment*

GALEN LOWE ART & ANTIQUES

Japanese and Asian folk art,
antiques, and textiles.
Galen Lowe
102 West Roy St.
Seattle, WA 98119
Tel: 206-270-8888
info@galenlowe.com
www.galenlowe.com
☺ *Tuesday – Saturday, 10:30 a.m. –*
5:30 p.m.

PAUL STEINHACKER – EARLY TRIBAL ARTS

Antique African, Oceanic, American
Indian, Eskimo, and Tibetan arts.
Appraisals, consulting. Est. 1968
Paul Steinhacker
2900 First Ave., #P-505
Seattle, WA 98121
Tel: 206-728-0410
PaulSTart9@aol.com
☺ *By appointment*

CURTRIGHT AND SON TRIBAL ART

Northwest Coast basketry and
sculpture, photographs, and historic
paintings. Material culture from all
of North America. Appraisals, sales,
purchases.
Jack G. Curtright
751 St. Helens Ave.
Tacoma, WA 98402
Tel: 253-383-2969
tyeejack@yahoo.com
www.curtrightson.com
☺ *Thursday – Saturday, 11 a.m. – 4 p.m.*

Tribal Art in WESTERN NORTH AMERICA

Tribal Art in **WESTERN NORTH AMERICA**

LUMMI ISLAND TRADING COMPANY

Antique baskets, art and artifacts from the Columbia River area – Oregon and Washington; the Northwest Coast and Alaska.

Penny Guest and Jim McGlinn
2129 G Street
Washougal, WA 98671
Tel: 360-835-3909
lummiis@aol.com
www.lummiislandtrading.com
☺ *By appointment*

BRITISH COLUMBIA
DORIAN RAE COLLECTION

Southeast Asian and West African art and artifacts

Dorian Rae
410 Howe Street
Vancouver, BC V6C 1A5
Tel: 604-874-6100
Fax: 604-874-6115
info@dorianraecollection.com
www.dorianraecollection.com
☺ *By appointment*

DOUGLAS REYNOLDS GALLERY

Historical and contemporary Northwest Coast art – carvings, masks, textiles, basketry.

Douglas Reynolds
2335 Granville St.
Vancouver, BC V6H 3G4
Tel: 604-731-9292
Fax: 604-731-9293
drg@axion.net
www.douglasreynoldsgallery.com
☺ *Monday – Saturday, 10 a.m. – 6 p.m.; Sunday, noon – 5 p.m.*

ANNUAL SHOWS AND SALES
GREATER LOS ANGELES AREA
LOS ANGELES ASIAN & TRIBAL ART SHOW

Antique Asian and tribal art and textiles

Santa Monica Civic Auditorium
Santa Monica, CA
Produced by Caskey-Lees Productions
P.O. Box 1409
Topanga, CA 90290
Tel: 310-455-2886
Fax: 310-455-1951
info@caskeylees.com
www.caskeylees.com
☺ *Annually in September*

SANTA MONICA INDIAN ART SHOW

American Indian, pre-Columbian, Western, and Spanish colonial art

Santa Monica Civic Auditorium
Santa Monica, CA
Produced by K.R. Martindale Show Management
1154 Grant Ave.
Venice, CA 90291
Tel: 310-822-9145
krmartindale@mac.com
www.krmartindale.com
www.americanindianartshow.com
☺ *Annually in May*

SAN FRANCISCO BAY AREA
AUCTIONS BY THE BAY

Occasional sales of tribal and pre-Columbian art.

Gregory Ghent
2700 Saratoga Street
Alameda, CA 94501
Tel: 510-740-0220 ext. 0
gregoryghent@auctionsbythebay.com
www.auctionsbythebay.com

BONHAMS & BUTTERFIELDS

Auctioneers and appraisers of Native American and tribal art.

Jim Haas
220 San Bruno Avenue
San Francisco, CA 94103
Tel: 415-503-3294
jim.haas@bonhams.com
www.bonhams.com
☺ *Two sales a year, typically in June and December*

MARIN INDIAN ART SHOW

Antique American Indian, pre-Columbian, Spanish Colonial, and contemporary American Indian art

Marin Civic Center
San Rafael, CA
Produced by K.R. Martindale Show Management
1154 Grant Ave.
Venice, CA 90291
Tel: 310-822-9145
krmartindale@mac.com
www.krmartindale.com
www.americanindianartshow.com
☺ *Annually in February*

THE SAN FRANCISCO ARTS OF PACIFIC ASIA SHOW

Antique Asian, Indonesian, and Pacific art

Fort Mason Center
San Francisco, CA
Produced by Caskey-Lees Productions
P.O. Box 1409
Topanga, CA 90290
Tel: 310-455-2886
info@caskeylees.com
www.caskeylees.com
☺ *Annually in February*

THE SAN FRANCISCO TRIBAL & TEXTILE ARTS SHOW

Antique tribal art, textiles, and folk art.

Fort Mason Center
San Francisco, CA
Produced by Caskey-Lees Productions
P.O. Box 1409
Topanga, CA 90290
Tel: 310-455-2886
info@caskeylees.com
www.caskeylees.com
☺ *Annually in February*

Additional multi-dealer shows are held by San Francisco Tribal and Los Angeles Tribal on an occasional basis. See their websites for details.

www.sftribal.com
www.latribal.com

SPECIALTY BOOKSELLERS
ETHNOGRAPHIC ARTS PUBLICATIONS

Rare and out-of-print books on the tribal arts of peoples around the world.

Arnold Rogoff
1040 Erica Road
Mill Valley, CA 94941
Tel: 415-383-2998
eap@tribalartbooks.com
www.tribalartbooks.com
☺ *By appointment*

AKSHARA BOOKS

Books on art, ethnology, and history for Latin America and Asia.

PO Box 22387
Seattle, WA 98122
akshara@akshara.com
☺ *Email only*

Tribal Art in WESTERN NORTH AMERICA

Booksellers / Photographers / Conservators

Tribal Art in **WESTERN NORTH AMERICA**

LOUIS COLLINS BOOKS

Rare scholarly and out-of-print books on world anthropology, tribal art, and global ethnographica

Louis Collins
1211 East Denny Way
Seattle, WA 98122
Tel: 206-323-3999
collinsbooks@collinsbooks.com
www.collinsbooks.com
☺ *Monday – Friday, noon – 5 p.m.; or by appointment*

PHOTOGRAPHERS
DON TUTTLE PHOTOGRAPHY

Ethnographic art, textile, and rug photography and ad design.

Don Tuttle
1456 63rd Street
Emeryville, CA 94608
Tel: 510-547-8509
dontut@earthlink.net
By appointment

AMERICAN PHOTO

Fine art transparencies from 35 mm to 8x10.

Q Siebenthal
1102 1/2 S. La Cienega Blvd.
Los Angeles, CA 90035
Tel: 310-289-8900
mrq@dslextreme.com
☺ *Tuesday – Friday, 9:30 a.m.– 3 p.m.; and Saturday mornings.*

RICHARD TODD PHOTOGRAPHY

Specializing in museum-quality photographing of tribal art, costume, sculpture, festivals

Richard Todd
1716 North Vista St.
Los Angeles, CA 90046
Tel: toll free 877-332-4478
richardtodd@dfbgcards.com

McCUE

Photography of tribal art for publication and advertising.

Scott McCue
83 Orinda Way
Orinda, CA 94563
Tel/Fax: 925-253-1719
info@mccuetribalart.com
www.mccuetribalart.com
☺ *By appointment*

DENNIS ANDERSON PHOTOGRAPHY

"Lighting that shows the soul of the piece"

Dennis Anderson
680 Pt. San Pedro Road
San Rafael, CA 9490
Tel: 415-457-1998
www.bluewaterpictures.com
☺ *By appointment*

BENGTSON PHOTOGRAPHY

Photography, including tribal objects and textiles.

Robert Bengtson
200 Gate 5 Road, suite 109
Sausalito, CA 94965
Tel: 415-332-7841
rb@bengtsonphoto.com
www.bengtsonphoto.com
☺ *By appointment*

CONSERVATION AND MOUNTING
ART BOX

Conservation, framing, restoration and stabilization of ethnographic material.

Michael D. Stevenson
Los Angeles, CA
Tel: 818-763-6939
laartbox@mac.com
www.laartbox.com
☺ *By appointment*

ALBERTO BRATSLAVSKY
Conservation of pre-Columbian, Asian, and African art.
Los Angeles, CA
Tel: 818-545-8030
☺ *By appointment*

GOLBERG RESTORATION CO.
Museum-quality conservation and restoration of paintings and objects of art
Rafail and Bolina Golberg
411 Westmount Dr.
Los Angeles, CA 90048
Tel: 310-652-0735
Cell: 310-435-9463
info@restorationworld.com
www.restorationworld.com
☺ *Monday – Friday, 10 a.m. – 6 p.m.; Saturday by appointment*

VERA INDENBAUM
Antique textile conservation
Los Angeles, CA
Tel: 310-836-3252
veraindenbaum@sbcglobal.net
☺ *By appointment*

SAAR STUDIO
Conservation and restoration of heirlooms and antiques.
711 North Harbor Avenue
Los Angeles, CA 90046
Tel: 323-653-1984
☺ *By appointment*

ABRIGHT & TARANTINO CERAMIC
Conservation, repair, and mounting
Bill Abright and Claudia Tarantino
190 Oak Avenue
San Anselmo, CA 94960
Tel: 415-454-1124
☺ *By appointment*

OTHER OPTIONS
Custom mounting and pedestals.
Sheridan Oakes
537 Grove St.
San Francisco, CA 94102
Tel: 415-861-2370
☺ *By appointment*

TRACY POWER OBJECTS CONSERVATION
Conservation and repair
Tracy Power
San Francisco, CA 94110
Tel: 415-824-8762
tracypower@earthlink.net
☺ *By appointment*

FARROW RESTORATION
Art restoration
Al and Erik Farrow
19 G Lovell Ave.
San Rafael, CA 94901
Tel: 415-485-5524
☺ *By appointment*

MICHAEL LEACH ENTERPRISES
Conservation, repair and mounting
Michael Leach
17 Lovell Avenue
San Rafael, CA 94901
Tel: 415-456-9560
☺ *By appointment*

APPRAISAL AND EXPERTISE
PHILANTHROPIA SOCIETY
A non-profit organization that receives and distributes intellectual and cultural property to institutions for educational use.
8890 Cypress Avenue
Cotati, CA 94931
Tel: 707-794-8087
☺ *By appointment*

Tribal Art in WESTERN NORTH AMERICA

Tribal Art in **WESTERN NORTH AMERICA**

GREGORY GHENT

Appraisal of pre-Columbian, tribal, modern, and contemporary art.

    Richmond, CA
    Tel: 510-232-0818
    gregoryghent@hotmail.com
    www.gregoryghent.com
☺ *By appointment*

SUSAN LERER, A.S.A. AND JENNIFER LIEBERMAN, TRIBAL ART APPRAISERS

Tribal art appraisal

    Susan Lerer
    Los Angeles, CA
    Tel: 323-936-0123
    slerer@susanlerer.com
    www.susanlerer.com
☺ *By appointment*

ANTONIO F. RUVOLO, Ph.D

Consulting, acquisition, research.

    Tel: 415-454-7930
    afrphd@yahoo.com
☺ *By appointment*

WORLDLY GOODS

Researcher, author, consultant, appraiser. Writing essays for museums, collectors, and dealers.

    Benson Lanford
    Ashland, OR
    Tel: 541-552-0320
    benlan@mind.net
☺ *By appointment*

ORGANIZATIONS

ATADA

Professional organization of dealers and collectors of tribal and American Indian art. Membership includes a quarterly newsletter.

    San Francisco, CA
    Tel: 415-863-3173
    acek33@aol.com
    www.atada.org

ETHNIC ARTS COUNCIL OF LOS ANGELES

A free-standing organization that sponsors lectures, tours, and trips for all aspects of ethnic art. Membership includes dealers, collectors, and other interested individuals. The council also provides grants for educational programs for museum exhibitions and events.

    PO Box 3771
    Beverly Hills, CA 90212
    Tel: 310-454-7851

FRIENDS OF ETHNIC ART

A non-profit, open-membership educational organization that offers slide lectures and other programs to expand knowledge and public awareness of human expression in traditional Native arts. Membership includes scholars, artists, museum professionals, private collectors and other enthusiasts.

    PO Box 192430
    San Francisco, CA 94119-2430
    Tel: 415-487-8706
    info@friendsofethnicart.org
    www.friendsofethnicart.org

LOS ANGELES TRIBAL

An association of dealers specializing in tribal art from Asia, Africa, Oceania, and the Americas.

    578 Washington Blvd. #555
    Marina Del Rey, CA 90292
    Tel: 800-923-1653
    www.latribal.com

SAN FRANCISCO TRIBAL

An association of dealers specializing in tribal art from Asia, Africa, Oceania, and the Americas.

    info@sftribal.com
    www.sftribal.com

Editor in Chief:
Jonathan Fogel

Associate Editor:
Alex Copeland

Editorial Assistance:
Christina Murray

Copy Editor:
Bob Christoph

Circulation:
Irene Strandenes (North America)
tribalmagazine@pacbell.net
Françoise Barrier (Europe)
info@primedia.be

Pre-Press:
Zetacolor, Milan

Printing:
Cassochrome, Waregem, Belgium

Publisher:
Alex Arthur

For advertising information in upcoming Eastern and Central North America and Pacific editions, please contact Jonathan Fogel at 415.431.8341 or at jmfogel@pacbell.net.

ISBN: 2-9600390-2-5

INDEX OF ADVERTISERS

Bonhams 1793
& BUTTERFIELDS
AUCTIONEERS & APPRAISERS

Native American, Pre-Columbian and Tribal Art

Inquiries
Jim Haas +1 (415) 503 3294
jim.haas@bonhams.com

For further information, complimentary
auction estimates or to view and order
catalogs, visit www.bonhams.com/us
or call +1 (800) 223 2854

Bonhams & Butterfields
220 San Bruno Avenue
San Francisco
California 94103
+1 (415) 861 7500
+1 (415) 861 8951 fax
www.bonhams.com/us

TRIBALMANIA.com

SANTA CRUZ, CALIFORNIA

831 336 3015 BY APPOINTMENT

ANCESTRAL FIGURE - MARQUESAS ISLANDS

LACY PRIMITIVE AND FINE ART

SAN FRANCISCO
ARTS OF PACIFIC ASIA SHOW

90 INTERNATIONAL ANTIQUES & ASIAN ART DEALERS EXHIBITING

ANNUALLY IN FEBRUARY Fort Mason Center, Festival Pavilion

SAN FRANCISCO
TRIBAL & TEXTILE ARTS
SHOW
FINE ART OF NATIVE CULTURES

"A must see, the oldest and largest fair of it's kind in the world"

108 INTERNATIONAL DEALERS EXHIBITING PRE-1940 TEXTILES & TRIBAL ARTS

ANNUALLY IN FEBRUARY Fort Mason Center, Festival Pavilion

LOS ANGELES
ASIAN & TRIBAL ARTS
SHOW

70 ART & ANTIQUES OF MAINLAND, CENTRAL & SOUTHEAST ASIA, AFRICA, INDONESIA, THE OCEANIC ISLANDS, PHILIPPINES & THE AMERICAS

ANNUALLY IN SEPTEMBER Santa Monica Civic Auditorium

Photos: Art of Percepolis, Bodhicitta, Michael Hamson, R. Franklin Hort Oriental Rugs, Huber Primitive Art, Andres Moraga

CASKEY-LEES Producers of Quality Fine Art & Antique Fairs Since 1985

PO Box 1409 Topanga, CA 90290 310 455 2886 info@caskeylees.com

www.caskeylees.com

Santa Monica and The Annual Marin Indian Art Shows

KR Martindale Show Management Presents

Mid May
Santa Monica Indian Art Show
Santa Monica, CA | Civic Auditorium

Last weekend of February
The Annual Marin Indian Art Show
San Rafael, CA | Marin Center & Embassy Suites

310.822.9145 krmartindale@mac.com • www.krmartindale.com

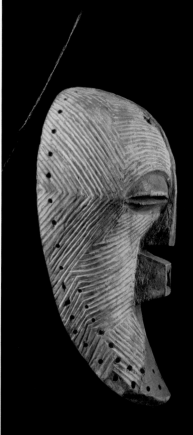

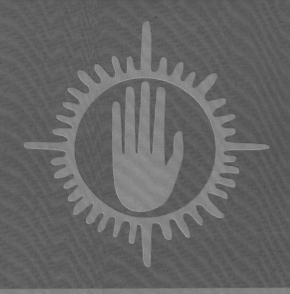

FRIENDS OF ETHNIC ART

Friends of Ethnic Art was founded in 1974 to provide a focus in the Bay Area for interest in the traditional arts of the **Africa, Oceania, and the Americas.**

It is a non-profit, educational, open-membership organization that offers slide lectures and other programs to expand awareness of human expression in these traditional native arts.

FEA has cooperative relationships with museums and universities in Northern California. The membership includes scholars, artists, museum professionals, dealers, private collectors and other enthusiasts drawn to this field.

Members of FEA enjoy:

Lectures by visiting scholars

Quarterly Newsletter notifying members of lectures and related events of AOA interest

Visits and field trips to private collections, museums and galleries

Annual party and tribal art auction of donated art objects

www.friendsofethnicart.org

P.O. Box 192430 San Francisco CA 94119 415.487.8706

Los Angeles
TRIBAL
(formerly Asian & Tribal Art-Los Angeles)

An association of
dealers specializing in
the tribal arts of Asia,
Africa, Oceania, and
the Americas

Anthropos Fine Art
(800) 243-2138

James Caswell - Historia
(310) 394-3384

Philip Garaway
(310) 577-8555

Michael Hamson Oceanic Art
(310) 373-1392

**Mark A. Johnson
Asian & Tribal Art**
(800) 923-1653

Leonard Kalina Fine Arts
(310) 399-0136

Lacy Primitive & Fine Art
(310) 271-0807

**Jerry Solomon
Asian & Tribal Arts**
(323) 876-2183

**Michael Sorafine
Primitive Arts**
(323) 930-1822

Stendahl Galleries
(323) 876-7740

Kent Watters
(310) 403-0507

www.latribal.com
1 (800) 923-1653